DAVE RAMSEY'S

FINANCIAL *Peace*®

MILITARY EDITION

*"The rich rule over the poor,
and the borrower is slave to the lender."*

Proverbs 22:7 (NIV)

MILLIONS
of Lives Changed
Since 1994

This publication is designed to provide accurate and authoritative information with regard to the subject matter covered. It is sold with the understanding that the publisher is not engaged in rendering legal, accounting, or other professional advice. If legal advice or other expert professional assistance is required, the services of a competent professional person should be sought.

—From a Declaration of Principles jointly adopted by a Committee of the American Bar Association and a Committee of Publishers and Associations

Published by Lampo Press. For more information, please visit our website at daveramsey.com/military.

Table of
CONTENTS

What would it be like?

What would your life be like if you had no payments? No credit card payments. No car payments. No home equity loan payments. Not even a house payment.

How much could you save and invest? How much could you blow and just have fun with? How much could you give? What if every dollar you brought home represented an *opportunity* for the future instead of an *obligation* to the past?

What kind of difference would it make to your family, your community, or your church if you were totally, completely, 100% debt-free?

How you spend your money tells a story. It's a story about what is important to you, about what really matters in your life. It's a story about where your heart is. Jesus said, "For where your treasure is, there your heart will be also" (Matthew 6:21). So it's time to pull out your checkbook and answer a hard question: Where's your heart?

If the story your financial life is telling is a lot different than the story your heart yearns for, then we've got good news: You can change the story. And you can start *right now*.

What you're going to learn in *Financial Peace University* (FPU) isn't just about saving money or getting out of debt or building up a healthy retirement—although those are all great things you'll do with this material. In fact, the goal isn't really about money at all. It's about living and giving the way God designed you to. It's about strengthening your marriage and teaching your kids. It's about leaving a legacy and being the change agent in your family tree. Basically, it's about learning what to do with everything God's entrusted to you.

FPU gives you the one thing the average American family is missing for their money: a plan. We can provide the "what" and the "how," but there's something you've got to bring to the table if you want this to work. You've got to bring your "why."

Why are you doing this? Why are you cracking open this book and starting this class? Why are you giving up a couple of hours a week for nine weeks to talk about money? Why do you want to change your story, and what will it look like when you're done?

There is a reason you're here.

There is a story to be told.

Let's get started!

Meet the Team

DAVE RAMSEY is America's trusted voice on money and business. More than 4.5 million people have participated in his financial programs. His nationally syndicated radio program, *The Dave Ramsey Show*, is heard by more than 12 million listeners each week on more than 575 radio stations and digitally through podcasts, online audio streaming, and a 24-hour online streaming video channel. He's authored seven best-selling books: *Financial Peace, More Than Enough, The Total Money Makeover, EntreLeadership, Dave Ramsey's Complete Guide to Money, Smart Money Smart Kids*, and *The Legacy Journey*.

By age 26, Dave had established a $4 million real estate portfolio, only to lose it all by age 30. Following his bankruptcy, Dave set out to learn God's ways of handling money. Using the wisdom he gained, he rebuilt his financial life. Dave now devotes himself to teaching others how to be responsible with their money so they can retire with dignity and give generously to others. You can follow Dave on Twitter at @DaveRamsey.

RACHEL CRUZE

As a seasoned communicator and Ramsey Personality, Rachel Cruze has been speaking to groups as large as 10,000 for more than a decade. The daughter of Dave Ramsey, she joined Ramsey Solutions in 2010 and uses the knowledge and experiences from growing up in the Ramsey household to educate others on handling their money wisely and staying out of debt. Rachel coauthored the #1 national best-selling book *Smart Money Smart Kids* with her dad. Her new book, *Love Your Life, Not Theirs*, released October 2016. You can follow Rachel on Twitter and Instagram at @RachelCruze and online at rachelcruze.com, youtube.com/rachelcruze, or facebook.com/rachelramseycruze.

JON ACUFF

Jon Acuff is the author of five books, including the *New York Times* best seller *Start* and the *Wall Street Journal* best seller *Quitter*. He is a keynote speaker at events across the country.

CHRIS HOGAN

A popular and dynamic speaker on the topics of personal finance, retirement and leadership, Chris Hogan helps people across the country develop successful strategies to manage their money in both their personal lives and businesses. He is the host of the Retire Inspired Podcast and the author of *Retire Inspired: It's Not an Age. It's a Financial Number*, a #1 national best seller. For more than a decade, Chris has served at Ramsey Solutions as a trusted financial coach and Ramsey Personality. You can follow Chris on Twitter and Instagram at @ChrisHogan360 and online at chrishogan360.com or facebook.com/chrishogan360.

Tell Your Story

Week 1

What do you expect to be your greatest
challenge as you get started with FPM?

_____

_____

_____

_____

_____

_____

_____

_____

_____

_____

_____

DATE

SUPER
SAVING

COMMON SENSE FOR YOUR DOLLARS AND CENTS

We're not a nation of savers. The typical American could not even cover a $5,000 emergency without having to borrow money. And big purchases? Nothing a swipe of the plastic can't take care of, right?

In *Super Saving*, Dave blasts through the hype and reveals the reasons why you should save money, how to be prepared for emergencies, and how to build genuine wealth—without luck or the lottery! More than that, Dave will truly get you excited about saving. Impossible? Not when you start *Super Saving*!

> *If you live like no one
> else, later you can live
> like no one else.*
>
> —DAVE RAMSEY

THE SEVEN BABY STEPS

There is a process for winning with money over time. No matter where you are today, whether you're financially secure or financially distressed, these Baby Steps will walk you step by step toward financial peace.

BABY STEP 1 Save $1,000 in a beginner emergency fund. ($500 if your income is under $20,000 per year.)

BABY STEP 2 Pay off all debt (except the house) using the debt snowball.

BABY STEP 3 Put 3–6 months of expenses in savings.

BABY STEP 4 Invest 15% of your household income into Roth IRAs/Roth TSPs and pre-tax retirement plans.

BABY STEP 5 Save for your children's college education using tax-favored plans.

BABY STEP 6 Pay off the house early.

BABY STEP 7 Build wealth and give!

Saving Basics

BABY STEP 1

_____ *in the bank.*

America consistently has one of the worst personal savings rates of all the nations of the world.

Saving must become a_____.

This is your first goal. Attack it and get it done fast.

You must pay yourself_____.

Give, save, and then pay _____.

Saving money is about_____ and _____.

Building wealth is not evil or wrong. Money is _____.

For the love of money is a root of all kinds of evil.

—1 TIMOTHY 6:10

_____

Christian author Larry Burkett once said, "The only difference between saving and hoarding is _____."

66

Making money is much harder to do if, deep down, you suspect it to be a morally reprehensible activity.

—RABBI DANIEL LAPIN

It is the Christian's spiritual_____ to take dominion over money. If we don't, we surrender God's resources to the enemy!

In the house of the wise are stores of choice food and oil, but a foolish man devours all he has.

— PROVERBS 21:20 (NIV84)

Why Save?

You should save for three basic reasons:

- _____ fund
- _____
- _____ building

Emergency Fund

_____ events do occur—expect it!

Remember, we just said that Baby Step 1, the beginner emergency fund, is $_____ in the bank (or $500 if your household income is below $20,000 per year).

Remember, you will pay off all consumer debt in Baby Step 2 before starting Baby Step 3.

BABY STEP 3

_____ *months of expenses in savings.*

A great place to keep your emergency fund is in a _____ _____ account from a mutual fund company.

Your emergency fund is not an _____; it is _____.

Do not _____ this fund for purchases!

The $1,000 emergency fund is your _____ savings priority. *Do it quickly!*

Money Market Accounts can be opened at your local bank or credit union. Be sure to get one that gives you check-writing privileges.

Murphy's Law: Whatever can go wrong, will go wrong.

Don't **DRIVE** yourself broke!

LET'S SAY an average car payment = $492 a month for 63 months.

WHAT IF you put that $492 into a cookie jar each month? You'd be able to **pay cash** for a $4,900 car in just **10 months!**

If a teenager takes this to heart early and never has a car payment throughout his whole life, can you imagine how wealthy he could become just from this one decision?

Purchases

Instead of _____ to purchase, pay cash by using a _____ fund approach.

FOR EXAMPLE ...

If you borrow to purchase a $_____ dining room set, the furniture store will probably sell your loan to a finance company.

This means you will have borrowed at _____% with payments of $_____ per month for _____ months. So, you will pay a total of $_____ for that set.

But if you save the same $_____ per month for only _____ months, you will be able to pay cash.

Daily decisions make a **HUGE** impact!

EXPENSE	COST PER DAY	COST PER MONTH	IF INVESTED AT 12% FROM AGE 16 TO 76
BOTTLED WATER	$2	$60	$7,825,768
GOURMET COFFEE	$5	$150	$19,564,358
LUNCH (5 days/week)	$8	$160	$20,868,640

Is it worth the cost in the long run?

Wealth Building

_____ is a key ingredient.

Building wealth is a _____,
not a _____.

_____ years of saving $_____ per month, every
month, at _____% will build to $_____.

_____-_____ _____
withdrawals are a good way to build in discipline.

Compound interest is a mathematical
_____.

You must start _____!

The Story of
BEN & ARTHUR
And the power of compound interest

Ben Invests	Total	Age	Arthur Invests	Total
2,000	2,240	19	0	0
2,000	4,749	20	0	0
2,000	7,558	21	0	0
2,000	10,706	22	0	0
2,000	14,230	23		
2,000	18,178	24	**ARTHUR STARTS LATE**	
2,000	22,599	25		
2,000	27,551	26	0	0
	30,857	27	2,000	2,240
	34,560	28	2,000	4,749
BEN STOPS SAVING!	38,708	29	2,000	7,558
	43,352	30	2,000	10,706
0	48,554	31	2,000	14,230
0	54,381	32	2,000	18,178
0	60,907	33	2,000	22,599
0	68,216	34	2,000	27,551
0	76,802	35	2,000	33,097
0	85,570	36	2,000	39,309
0	95,383	37	2,000	46,266
0	107,339	38	2,000	54,058
0	120,220	39	2,000	62,785
0	134,646	40	2,000	72,559
0	150,804	41	2,000	83,506
0	168,900	42	2,000	95,767
0	189,168	43	2,000	109,499
0	211,869	44	2,000	124,879
0	237,293	45	2,000	142,104
0	265,768	46	2,000	161,396
0	297,660	47	2,000	183,004
0	333,379	48	2,000	207,204
0	373,385	49	2,000	234,308
0	418,191	50	2,000	264,665
0	468,374	51	2,000	298,665
0	524,579	52	2,000	336,745
0	587,528	53	2,000	379,394
0	658,032	54	2,000	427,161
0	736,995	55	2,000	480,660
0	825,435	56	2,000	540,579
0	924,487	57	2,000	607,688
0	1,035,425	58	2,000	682,851
0	1,159,676	59	2,000	767,033
0	1,298,837	60	2,000	861,317
0	1,454,698	61	2,000	966,915
0	1,629,261	62	2,000	1,085,185
0	1,824,773	63	2,000	1,217,647
0	2,043,746	64	2,000	1,366,005
0	2,288,996	65	2,000	1,532,166
	$2,288,996			**$1,532,166**

Ben starts saving money at 19 years old.
He saves $2,000 a year until age 26, a total of eight years. After that, he never invests another dime.

Arthur starts saving money at 27 years old.
He saves $2,000 a year until age 65, almost his entire life.

At the end of the story,
Ben, who invested only $16,000, ends up with $2,288,996! But Arthur, who put in $78,000, ends up with $1,532,166.

· ·

Just because he started early,

Ben came out ahead by over
$700,000!

If you are currently struggling, behind on your bills or in collections, watch the free *Credit Sharks in Suits* lesson online in the Military Toolkit.

daveramsey.com/military/toolkit/signin

Exponential Growth

The rate of return, or _____ rate, is important.

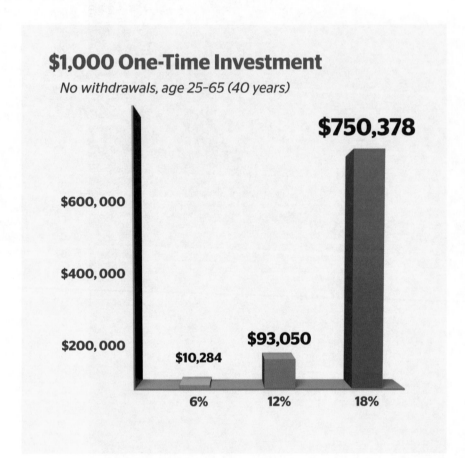

$1,000 One-Time Investment

No withdrawals, age 25–65 (40 years)

$600,000

$400,000

$200,000

$10,284

$93,050

$750,378

6%   12%   18%

QUICK-START BUDGET

It's time to take your first step toward financial peace with this simple, one-page Quick-Start Budget, found in the back of this book. This form takes your expenses down to the bare necessities and helps you get your arms around your income—and your outgo. Don't worry about listing out your debts yet; we'll get to that later. For now, we just want to get you started with the basics.

Go from pen and paper to high tech with our FREE online budget tool, EveryDollar! You can access and create a free EveryDollar account online through your Military Toolkit. Enter your income then assign every dollar of your income to the personalized budget groups. That's all you have to do to set up your first budget!

One-Minute Takeaway

What jumped out at you in this lesson? How can this affect your story?

_____

_____

_____

_____

_____

Small Group Discussion

True life-change happens when you open up and work through this material together. Break up into discussion groups of no more than 20 people to talk through the following questions. Be honest in your answers!

1 If you follow the plan outlined throughout FPM, the next nine weeks will change your money—and your behaviors with money—forever. However, if it were easy, everyone would have financial peace! Talk about one or two things you are worried about having to deal with or something you are looking forward to achieving as you work through the program.

2 American families typically save far less of their income than those in other countries. In what specific area(s) could you be—or would you want to be—more diligent about saving?

3 Dave says, "I'm positive—emergencies are going to happen!" Talk about a financial emergency you've had over the last few years. How would the situation have been different if you'd had an emergency fund specifically for these types of expenses?

4 Dave recommends building sinking funds into your budget to cover big purchases and future expenses. Talk about some expenses you've had in the past that could have been less stressful with a sinking fund.

5 The time has come for all of us to start dreaming bigger. Imagine yourself debt free with an emergency fund in place, fully funding retirement and college investments, and writing the check to pay off the house. What are some things you can't wait to do with the money—and freedom—you've secured for yourself?

This Week's Homework

Personal finance is 20% head knowledge and 80% behavior. Take charge of your financial behaviors by completing the following tasks this week. Be sure to work with your spouse or accountability partner where noted!

☑ **Register for the online tools.**
Visit the Military Toolkit online at daveramsey.com/military/toolkit/create-profile and sign up for the additional online tools and resources.

☑ **Complete the Quick-Start Budget form.**
You can use the paper form from the back of this book, or download a printable version online in the Military Toolkit. However you choose to do your budget, bring the completed form to class next week for your facilitator to review.

☑ **Complete the Financial Reality Check.**
Fill out the Financial Reality Check on the next page. Be sure to bring the results to class next week.

☑ **Extra Credit**: If you are facing debt collectors or considering bankruptcy, watch the *Credit Sharks in Suits* lesson in your Military Toolkit.

Financial Reality Check

Financial peace is closer than you think! But before we get started, let's put a stake in the ground where your current finances stand. This is information you're going to look back on five years from now, and you'll be amazed at how far you've come! Answer the questions below, and be honest!

What's your total non-mortgage debt?

This includes any money you owe on anything, including student loans, credit cards, car loans, second mortgages, home equity loans, etc. This is the total of everything except a first mortgage.

TOTAL

How much liquid cash do you have available?

This is the cash you could get your hands on immediately, like savings, checking and money market accounts. This does not include home equity lines of credit, cash advances or retirement funds.

TOTAL

How many open credit card accounts do you have?

Remember, even if you pay off a card, the account is still open. To truly be rid of it forever, you must formally request that the credit company or bank officially close the account.

TOTAL

On a scale of 1–10, rate the following emotions in regard to your personal finances:

	1	2	3	4	5	6	7	8	9	10
Fear	○	○	○	○	○	○	○	○	○	○
Anxiety	○	○	○	○	○	○	○	○	○	○
Confidence	○	○	○	○	○	○	○	○	○	○
Hope	○	○	○	○	○	○	○	○	○	○
Peace	○	○	○	○	○	○	○	○	○	○

1	2	3	4	5	6	7	8	9	10
Practically None									Extremely High

The Secret to Saving Money

Most people don't save like they know they need to. Why? Because they have competing goals. The goal to save isn't a high enough priority to delay that purchase of the pizza, DVD player, new computer or china cabinet. So they purchase, buy, and consume all their dollars away or, worse yet, go into debt to buy these things.

That debt brings monthly payments that control our paychecks and make us say things like, "We just don't make enough to save any money!" Wrong, wrong, wrong! We do make enough to save money. We just aren't willing to quit spoiling ourselves with our little projects or pleasures to have enough left to save. It doesn't matter what you make—you can save money. It just has to become a big enough priority.

If a doctor told you that your child was dying and could only be saved with a $15,000 operation that your insurance would not cover and could only be performed nine months from today, could you save $15,000? Yes! Of course you could! You would sell things, stop any spending that wasn't required to survive, and take two extra jobs. For that short nine months, you would become a saving madman. You would give up virtually anything to accomplish that $15,000 goal. Saving would become a priority.

The secret to saving money is to make it a priority, and that is done only when you find some healthy anger or fear and use those emotions to guide your personal decisions. Then ask yourself: *Which bill is the most important? After tithing, whom should I pay first this month?* The answer is you!

Advertisers and marketers are great at affecting our emotions and making us see our wants as needs. It is time for this to stop! Emotions make great servants, but they are lousy masters. No matter how educated or sophisticated we are, if we're not saving then we're being ruled by emotions and not harnessing them.

So whether you are saving for college tuition, a vacation, new school clothes for the kids or anything else, start saving now! It's never too late!

KEY TERMS

Baby Steps: Dave Ramsey's seven-step process for winning with money

Compound Interest: Interest paid on both the principal and the accumulated value of previously accrued interest

Emergency Fund: Easily accessible savings set aside only for emergencies; a full emergency fund (Baby Step 3) is 3–6 months of expenses

Interest Rate: Percentage paid to a lender for the use of borrowed money

Money Market Mutual Fund: Essentially a savings account with a mutual fund company; earns slightly higher rate of return than a simple savings account through short-term mutual fund investments

Sinking Fund: A systematic way of saving money over time for a specific purchase; i.e., saving $400 a month for 10 months to buy a $4,000 car

Tell Your Story

Week 2

How would it feel to work with a spouse or partner as you start the budget process?

_____

_____

_____

_____

_____

_____

_____

_____

_____

_____

_____

_____

_____

_____

_____

_____

_____

_____
DATE

RELATING
WITH MONEY

NERDS AND FREE SPIRITS UNITE!

How we handle our money impacts every part of our lives.
It is a huge factor in marriage, a tremendous responsibility in
parenting, and a potential land mine for singles.

In *Relating With Money*, Dave and Rachel show couples how to
work together as a team, give singles some practical tips for
financial accountability, and help parents teach their children
about money from a young age. You'll discover that money is
rarely *just* about money. It is about so much more!

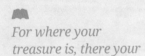

For where your treasure is, there your heart will be also.

—MATTHEW 6:21

Your behavior is the key to taking control of your money, and your behavior is tied to your relationships.

The flow of money in a household represents the _____ _____ under which that household operates.

Men, Women and Money

EMERGENCY FUND

Men: "It's boring and not _____ enough."

Women: "It's the most _____ key to our financial plan."

SHOPPING

Men get good deals by _____.
Men want to win.

Women get good deals by _____.
Women enjoy the process.

FINANCIAL PROBLEMS

Men lose _____-_____ because money usually represents a _____ to men.

Women face _____ or even _____ because money usually represents _____ to women.

Marriage and Money

The number-one cause of divorce in North America is _____ _____.

When you agree on your value system, you will reach a _____ in your marriage that you can experience no other way.

Nerds and Free Spirits

Who should do the financial decision-making in marriage? _____ of you!

The partner with the natural _____ can prepare the budget, but the decision-making must be done by _____.

The _____ likes doing the budget because it gives them control, and they feel like they are taking care of loved ones.

If money has the potential to be our worst area, then it also has the potential to be the best area of our marriage.

A couple with $10,000 in debt and no savings is twice as likely to divorce as a couple with no debt and $10,000 in savings.

—CNN

The _____ _____ feels controlled, not cared for, and can appear irresponsible to the Nerd.

The Nerd is not necessarily always the _____, and the Free Spirit is not necessarily always the _____.

Singles and Money

_____ _____ and fatigue can lead to poor money management.

Beware of _____ buying, which can be brought on by stress or even the "I owe it to _____" syndrome.

_____ often causes singles to go out and spend money they don't have just to be "out in the world."

STRATEGIES FOR SINGLES

A written plan gives the single person _____, self-accountability and _____.

Develop an _____ relationship.

This is someone with whom to discuss a major _____ and your _____.

Getting a reluctant spouse on board may be difficult, but it is crucial to your success.

Don't nag, whine and complain. Start by telling your spouse WHY you want to change your lives this way. Get them to dream with you!

Where there is no counsel, the people fall; but in the multitude of counselors there is safety.

—PROVERBS 11:14

Official Rules for the

BUDGET COMMITTEE

Meeting

RULES FOR THE
Nerd

Bring the budget in, have your say, and then shut up!

It's not a weekend summit. You have 17 minutes.

Insist that the Free Spirit mess with the budget!

RULES FOR THE
Free Spirit

You must come to the meeting!

You must give thoughtful input.

Never again use the phrase, "Whatever you want to do, honey."

It's absolutely essential that both spouses work as a team on the budget.

Nerds & Free Spirits Unite!

Kids and Money

Teaching your kids how to handle money is not the_____responsibility.
It is _____ responsibility!

Pay _____, not allowance.

A good man leaves an inheritance to his children's children.

—PROVERBS 13:22

Words are _____.

If you _____, you get paid; if you don't _____, you don't get paid.

Teach by _____.

Show them how you live _____ free, how insurance works, how an IRA works, etc.

AGE-APPROPRIATE STRATEGIES

If the children are very young, use a clear

_____ to save.

USE THREE ENVELOPES FOR AGES 5-12:

1. _____

2. _____

3. _____

Somewhere around 13–15 years old, open a

_____ _____ for the child and

teach him or her how to run it by monthly reviews.

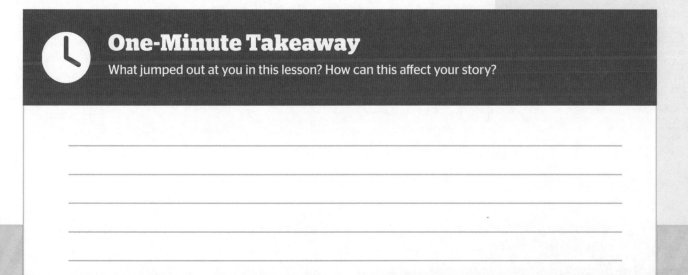

One-Minute Takeaway

What jumped out at you in this lesson? How can this affect your story?

Small Group Discussion

True life-change happens when you open up and work through this material together. Break up into discussion groups of no more than 20 people to talk through the following questions. Be honest in your answers!

1 Each person in the group should take 15 seconds to answer the following question: Throughout this program, you will be challenged to try things you've probably never done. Just for the next eight weeks, are you willing to commit yourself to the principles—even if you have disagreements? Why or why not?

2 Zig Ziglar says, "Show me your calendar and your checkbook, and I will tell you what is most important in your life." Take out your Quick-Start Budget and note the three areas where you spend the most money. What surprises you about your top three categories?

3 Do those three largest expenses accurately represent what is most important to you? If so, how does that feel? If not, what would you like your largest budget categories to be in the future?

Breakout Group Exercise

Break into smaller groups of 4–5 people to work through the following activity. Choose a leader to read through the exercise aloud and keep the group on task. Your facilitator will call the groups back together to report your findings.

Activity: *Nerd and Free Spirit Quiz*

Going one row at a time, fill in the bubble for the statement that best represents you. Add up your totals at the bottom and chart your score on page 33. **If you're here with your spouse,** they will use the additional quiz on the next page.

STATEMENT 1	OR		STATEMENT 2
You actually enjoy balancing the checkbook.	○	○	You'd rather balance a spoon on your nose than balance your checkbook.
Rules are important and should be followed.	○	○	Rules are more like suggestions to be considered.
You are always on time. Always.	○	○	You show up "on time." Give or take 15 minutes.
You spend more time planning the vacation than the vacation itself.	○	○	Vacations are more fun when the calendar's blank and you just "go."
Recipes should be precisely followed. Like rules.	○	○	Recipes are suggestions. Just do a dash here and a dash there.
You read the introductions of books. They're in there for a reason!	○	○	You skip introductions. Then it's like you read more!
You organize your shirts by color, or you will when you get home.	○	○	You're doing good just to get your shirts hung up.
You can't wait for Dave to teach about budgeting.	○	○	You're considering faking an illness the night of the budget lesson.
"Living for the moment" sounds irresponsible to you.	○	○	"Living for the moment" sounds like the soundtrack of your life.
Clutter is annoying and frustrates you.	○	○	It's not clutter; it's character!

Your Nerd Score **Your Free Spirit Score**

Activity: *Nerd and Free Spirit Quiz*

This second quiz sheet is provided for spouses only. Singles can skip right to the score sheet. **Going one row at a time,** fill in the bubble for the statement that best represents you. Add up your totals at the bottom and continue to the score sheet.

STATEMENT 1	OR		STATEMENT 2
You actually enjoy balancing the checkbook.	○	○	You'd rather balance a spoon on your nose than balance your checkbook.
Rules are important and should be followed.	○	○	Rules are more like suggestions to be considered.
You are always on time. Always.	○	○	You show up "on time." Give or take 15 minutes.
You spend more time planning the vacation than the vacation itself.	○	○	Vacations are more fun when the calendar's blank and you just "go."
Recipes should be precisely followed. Like rules.	○	○	Recipes are suggestions. Just do a dash here and a dash there.
You read the introductions of books. They're in there for a reason!	○	○	You skip introductions. Then it's like you read more!
You organize your shirts by color, or you will when you get home.	○	○	You're doing good just to get your shirts hung up.
You can't wait for Dave to teach about budgeting.	○	○	You're considering faking an illness the night of the budget lesson.
"Living for the moment" sounds irresponsible to you.	○	○	"Living for the moment" sounds like the soundtrack of your life.
Clutter is annoying and frustrates you.	○	○	It's not clutter; it's character!

Your Nerd Score **Your Free Spirit Score**

TEST ONE RESULTS

TEST RESULTS FOR_____

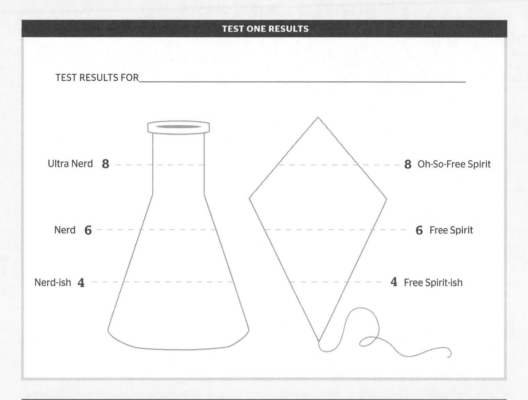

Ultra Nerd **8** - - - - - - - - - - - - - - - - - - - **8** Oh-So-Free Spirit

Nerd **6** - - - - - - - - - - - - - - - - - - - **6** Free Spirit

Nerd-ish **4** - - - - - - - - - - - - - - - - - - - **4** Free Spirit-ish

TEST TWO RESULTS (FOR COUPLES)

TEST RESULTS FOR_____

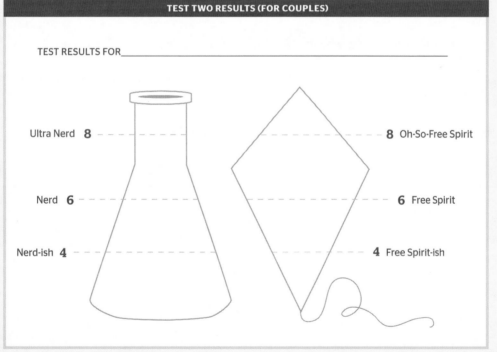

Ultra Nerd **8** - - - - - - - - - - - - - - - - - - - **8** Oh-So-Free Spirit

Nerd **6** - - - - - - - - - - - - - - - - - - - **6** Free Spirit

Nerd-ish **4** - - - - - - - - - - - - - - - - - - - **4** Free Spirit-ish

What your score says about you...

Nerd-ish (4-5)
You balance your checkbook regularly, shop only when things are on sale, and you got rid of your credit cards years ago.

Free Spirit-ish (4-5)
You've got a budget, but you can't remember the last time you actually looked at it.

Nerd (6-7)
When it comes to budgeting and paying down debt, all you do is win.

Free Spirit (6-7)
Budgets are for people who don't live in the now or really seize the day.

Ultra Nerd (8+)
You are a Nerd to the tenth degree.

Oh-So-Free Spirit (8+)
Budgets are for boring people.

DISCUSSION QUESTIONS

1. Tell your group where you landed: Nerd, Free Spirit or right in between? Does this surprise you? Why or why not?

2. Free Spirits, tell your group why the "Saving" category is so important.

3. Nerds, tell your group why the "Entertainment" category is so important.

4. Free Spirits, tell your group what unique strengths your Free Spiritedness brings to the table.

5. Nerds, tell your group what unique strengths your Nerdiness brings to the table.

This Week's Homework

Personal finance is 20% head knowledge and 80% behavior. Take charge of your financial behaviors by completing the following tasks this week. Be sure to work with your spouse or accountability partner where noted!

☑ **Identify your accountability partner.**
Singles: It's time to find your accountability partner. Make a short list of your top choices and get a commitment from someone this week!

Married Couples: Sign in to the online resources and download a copy of the Budget Committee Meeting rules. Be sure you both get a copy to review for this week's meeting!

☑ **Review your Quick-Start Budget together.**
Singles: Share your Quick-Start Budget with your new accountability partner and discuss what you've learned so far in FPM. Tell them about the Nerd/Free Spirit concept and identify which one you both are.

Married Couples: It's time to call your first Budget Committee Meeting! Talk about what you've learned so far in FPM and how you feel about your Quick-Start Budget. Identify and discuss the strengths and weaknesses you each bring to the table using the Nerd/Free Spirit model.

☐ **Register for the online tools.**
If you have not done so yet, sign up for the Military Toolkit at daveramsey.com/military/toolkit/create-profile for additional online tools and resources.

The Danger Zone

So the old joke goes: If you lend your brother-in-law $50 and he never talks to you again, was it worth the investment?

The joke may be funny, but experiencing this in real life is anything but funny. Just ask anyone who has experienced it firsthand. Loaning money to a friend or family member is a bad decision. You simply can't justify it.

Someone who lends money to a loved one has their heart—not their head—in the right place. It is okay to give money, but loaning money to someone with whom you have a relationship will lead to broken hearts and broken wallets.

Eventually, it has a way of destroying relationships because loaning money introduces guilt, judgment, and a lack of trust. Brothers and sisters grow apart. Parents and adult children begin to argue. It's just never a good situation.

Check out the statistics from a recent money and etiquette survey:

- 57% of people said they have seen a friendship or relationship ruined because one person didn't pay back the other.

- Almost 50% have loaned $100 or more to help someone, but 55% don't get repaid.

- 71% lend money to immediate family members, 57% to relatives, and 54% to friends.

One fact not quoted in the survey is that Thanksgiving dinner tastes 100% better when friends or relatives don't owe each other money! Eating with your master is different than eating with your family.

The turkey is more succulent, the mashed potatoes are creamier, the green beans are juicier, and the rolls melt in your mouth. Doesn't that sound delicious? And all because you didn't make the mistake of loaning money.

Think about it. When you've loaned money to a family member, how did you feel the next time you saw them?

A loan has a way of hanging over the head of both the lender and the borrower. There's a fog in the air every time you see that other person—and it's a fog that will only be cleared when the debt is repaid.

It starts out as an emotional decision. You want to help them—they are family, after all, right? Maybe guilt sets in. Maybe you're in a decent financial position and you're able to help out, so why not?

So you give in and make the loan. You probably have some type of loose agreement, like, "Just pay me back when you can"—which they interpret as, "Just pay me back sometime in the next 20 years."

KEY TERMS

Accountability: The quality or state of being accountable, liable or answerable

Free Spirit: A person who thinks that everything will work out fine; typically hates to deal with numbers

Nerd: A person who is picky about budgeting and numbers

Time Poverty: A situation in which a person is lacking time, which leads to stress

Value System: A person's priorities, beliefs and standards that affect how he or she views the world

If someone is in genuine need, it's great to help. If you help with money, make it a gift instead of a loan.

And that's where the awkwardness starts. Because, let's be honest, loaning money makes relationships awkward. Parents who lend their newly married daughter and her husband a down payment for a house think they are helping out the new family.

Soon, however, they are giving the young couple disapproving looks when an upcoming vacation, a car, or a new piece of furniture becomes more important than repaying the loan. This leads to nothing but resentment and pain on both sides. It is inevitable.

Don't fall into this trap and do this to people and relationships that mean something to you. If someone is in genuine need, it's great to help. If you help with money, make it a gift instead of a loan.

Think about how much more of an impact you can make by giving a gift,

rather than putting someone else in financial bondage to you. That's not only the healthiest option for their finances, but it's also the best option for your relationship.

If you can't afford to make it a gift, then it's not a good idea. Sit down with them and explore some other alternatives that will help them earn the money, whether it's a second job, selling stuff, or re-examining how much money they really need.

By not having an I.O.U. hanging over your head, you will keep your relationships strong.

Tell Your Story

Week 3

What are your initial thoughts or concerns as you look toward your first full budget?

_____

_____

_____

_____

_____

_____

_____

_____

_____

_____

_____

_____

_____

_____

_____

DATE

CASH FLOW PLANNING

THE NUTS AND BOLTS OF BUDGETING

Oh no! The dreaded B-word: budget! Many people are scared to death of the very idea of a budget. It drums up images of living on bread and water and a dull, dreary, no-frills way of life. That's not what we're talking about!

The truth is, the budget is your key to success! Like Dave says, money makes a fantastic servant, but it is a horrible master. And if you don't tell your money where to go and what to do, it will definitely master you the rest of your life. In *Cash Flow Planning*, you'll learn how to make your money work for you and how to put together a household budget that really works!

> *Be diligent to know the state of your flocks, and attend to your herds.*
>
> —PROVERBS 27:23

Budgeting Basics

Money is _____.

You must do a written _____ _____ plan every month.

> *For which of you, intending to build a tower, does not sit down first and count the cost, whether he has enough to finish it—lest . . . all who see it begin to mock him, saying, "This man began to build and was not able to finish"?*
>
> —LUKE 14:28–30

You have to _____ your bank account.

Overdrafts are a sign of _____ _____ and sloppy, lazy money habits.

If not managed and made to behave, the _____ card and the _____ card are certain to become budget busters.

The most popular method of banking by far is _____ banking.

Reasons We DON'T Do a Cash Flow Plan

MOST PEOPLE HATE THE WORD "BUDGET" FOR FOUR REASONS:

- It has a _____ and _____ connotation.

- It has been used to _____ them.

- They never had a budget that really _____.

- Paralysis from _____ of what they'll find.

CASH FLOW PLANS DO NOT WORK IF YOU:

- _____ things _____.

- _____ your plan.

- Don't actually _____ one.

- Don't actually _____ on it.

Your budget won't be perfect the first month or two. That's okay. The key is to be consistent and to learn from the mistakes! Don't worry; things will start to smooth out by the third month.

If you're struggling to maintain the Four Walls, check out the free *Credit Sharks in Suits* lesson online to learn how to get some traction with your budget.

daveramsey.com/military/toolkit/signin

The plans of the diligent lead surely to plenty, but those of everyone who is hasty, surely to poverty.

—PROVERBS 21:5

Reasons We SHOULD Do a Cash Flow Plan

A written plan removes the management by _____ from your finances.

THE FOUR WALLS:

Build up the Four Walls that protect your family by prioritizing _____, basic _____, shelter and utilities, and transportation.

> *But if anyone does not provide for his own, and especially those of his household, he has denied the faith and is worse than an unbeliever.*
>
> —1 TIMOTHY 5:8

Managed money feels like getting a _____.

A WRITTEN PLAN, IF ACTUALLY LIVED AND AGREED ON . . .

- Will remove many of the _____ _____ from your marriage.

- Will remove much of the _____, shame and _____ that may now be a part of buying necessities such as food or clothing.

- Will show if you are _____ on a certain area.

- Will give you a sense of _____ and _____ over money that you can't get any other way.

The easiest and most powerful plan is a _____-based plan using the _____ system.

> "Zero-based" does not mean your bank account should hit zero! Keep a pad or buffer of around $100 in your account to catch any little budget missteps.

BUDGET FORMS

Use the examples on the following pages as a guide. Dave covers these in the lessons, but there are several other forms available to help you master your money. You can find all the forms, our budget tutorials, and free budgeting tools in in the Military Toolkit. Ready to bring your budget forms to life? Create your budget online by signing up for your free EveryDollar account.

Monthly Cash Flow Plan

Cash flows in and out each month. Make sure you tell it where to go!

Monthly Take-Home Pay | 3,660

Add up budgeted column & enter here

These icons represent good options for cash envelopes

♥ CHARITY

	Spent	Budgeted
Tithes		410
Charity & Offerings		
*10-15% TOTAL		410

🐷 SAVING

	Spent	Budgeted
Emergency Fund		
Retirement Fund		
College Fund		
*10-15% TOTAL		

🏠 HOUSING

	Spent	Budgeted
First Mortgage/Rent		945
Second Mortgage		
Real Estate Taxes		
Repairs/Maint.		
Association Dues		
*25-35% TOTAL		945

⚙ UTILITIES

	Spent	Budgeted
Electricity		100
Gas		75
Water		55
Trash		
Phone/Mobile		124
Internet		40
Cable		
*5-10% TOTAL		394

🍎 FOOD

	Spent	Budgeted
✉ Groceries		600
✉ Restaurants		50
*5-15% TOTAL		650

👕 CLOTHING

	Spent	Budgeted
✉ Adults		75
✉ Children		75
✉ Cleaning/Laundry		
*2-7% TOTAL		150

🚗 TRANSPORTATION

	Spent	Budgeted
Gas & Oil		200
✉ Repairs & Tires		
License & Taxes		
Car Replacement		
Other _____		
*10-15% TOTAL		200

⚕ MEDICAL/HEALTH

	Spent	Budgeted
Medications		
Doctor Bills		50
Dentist		
Optometrist		
Vitamins		
Other _____		
Other _____		
*5-10% TOTAL		50

*Dave's Recommended Percentages

🛡 INSURANCE

	Spent	Budgeted
Life Insurance		38
Health Insurance		(work)
Homeowner/Renter		(escrow)
Auto Insurance		88
Disability Insurance		(work)
Identity Theft		12
Long-Term Care		NA
*10-25% TOTAL		138

👤 PERSONAL

	Spent	Budgeted
✉ Child Care/Sitter		
✉ Toiletries		
✉ Cosmetics/Hair Care		60
Education/Tuition		
Books/Supplies		
Child Support		
Alimony		
Subscriptions		
Organization Dues		
Gifts (inc. Christmas)		
✉ Replace Furniture		
✉ Pocket Money (His)		30
✉ Pocket Money (Hers)		30
Baby Supplies		
Pet Supplies		
Music/Technology		
Miscellaneous		
Other _____		
Other _____		
*5-10% TOTAL		120

🏃 RECREATION

	Spent	Budgeted
✉ Entertainment		50
Vacation		
*5-10% TOTAL		50

🦴 DEBTS

	Spent	Budgeted
Car Payment 1		310
Car Payment 2		
Credit Card 1 VISA		150
Credit Card 2 Home Depot		45
Credit Card 3 _____		
Credit Card 4 _____		
Credit Card 5 _____		
Student Loan 1		
Student Loan 2		
Student Loan 3		
Student Loan 4		
Other ___Hospital___		48
Other _____		
Other _____		
Other _____		
Other _____		

Your goal is 0% → | *5-10% TOTAL | | 553 |

Once you have completed filling out each category, subtract all category totals from your take-home pay.

Use the "income sources" form if necessary → TAKE-HOME PAY **3,660**

Add up totals from each category − CATEGORY TOTALS **3,660**

Remember— The goal of a zero-based budget is to get this number to zero = ZERO BALANCE **0**

Allocated Spending Plan

Don't let this one scare you. Managing your money week to week happens here!

Pay Period Dates	7/1 TO 7/14	7/15 TO 7/29	TO	TO
Pay Period Income	3,188	472		

Income
— Tithes
= Remaining to budget this pay period

♥ CHARITY

	Budgeted	Remaining	Budgeted	Remaining	Budgeted	Remaining	Budgeted	Remaining
Tithes	410	2778						
Charity & Offerings								

"Remaining" minus "Budgeted." Back & forth.

🐷 SAVING

	Budgeted	Remaining	Budgeted	Remaining	Budgeted	Remaining	Budgeted	Remaining
Emergency Fund								
Retirement Fund								
College Fund								

🏠 HOUSING

	Budgeted	Remaining	Budgeted	Remaining	Budgeted	Remaining	Budgeted	Remaining
First Mortgage/Rent	945	1833						
Second Mortgage								
Real Estate Taxes								
Repairs/Maint.								
Association Dues								
Other _____								

⚙ UTILITIES

	Budgeted	Remaining	Budgeted	Remaining	Budgeted	Remaining	Budgeted	Remaining
Electricity	100	1733						
Gas			75	397				
Water			55	342				
Trash								
Phone/Mobile			124	218				
Internet	40	1693						
Cable								
Other _____								

Pay Period Dates	7/1 TO 7/14	7/15 TO 7/29	TO	TO

When "Remaining" equals zero, you're done budgeting for this pay period.

🍎 FOOD

	Budgeted	Remaining	Budgeted	Remaining	Budgeted	Remaining	Budgeted	Remaining
✉ Groceries	450	1243	150	68				
✉ Restaurants	50	1193						

👕 CLOTHING

	Budgeted	Remaining	Budgeted	Remaining	Budgeted	Remaining	Budgeted	Remaining
✉ Adults	75	1118						
✉ Children	75	1043						
✉ Cleaning/Laundry								

🚗 TRANSPORTATION

	Budgeted	Remaining	Budgeted	Remaining	Budgeted	Remaining	Budgeted	Remaining
Gas and Oil	200	843						
✉ Repairs and Tires								
License and Taxes								
Car Replacement								
Other _____								
Other _____								

🩺 MEDICAL/HEALTH

	Budgeted	Remaining	Budgeted	Remaining	Budgeted	Remaining	Budgeted	Remaining
Medications								
Doctor Bills	50	793						
Dentist								
Optometrist								
Vitamins								
Other _____								
Other _____								
Other _____								
Other _____								

Allocated Spending Plan

Don't let this one scare you. Managing your money week to week happens here!

Pay Period Dates	7/1 TO 7/14	7/15 TO 7/29	TO	TO

🛡 INSURANCE

	Budgeted	Remaining	Budgeted	Remaining	Budgeted	Remaining	Budgeted	Remaining
Life Insurance			38	30				
Health Insurance								
Homeowner/Renter								
Auto Insurance	88	705						
Disability Insurance								
Identity Theft	12	693						
Long-Term Care								

👤 PERSONAL

	Budgeted	Remaining	Budgeted	Remaining	Budgeted	Remaining	Budgeted	Remaining
✉ Child Care/Sitter								
✉ Toiletries								
✉ Cosmetics	60	633						
Education/Tuition								
Books/Supplies								
Child Support								
Alimony								
Subscriptions								
Org. Dues								
Gifts (inc. Christmas)								
✉ Replace Furniture								
✉ Pocket Money (His)			30	0				
✉ Pocket Money (Hers)	30	603						
Baby Supplies								
Pet Supplies								
Music/Technology								
Miscellaneous								
Other _____								
Other _____								

Pay Period Dates	7/1 TO 7/14	7/15 TO 7/29	TO	TO

🏃 RECREATION

	Budgeted	Remaining	Budgeted	Remaining	Budgeted	Remaining	Budgeted	Remaining
✉ Entertainment	50	553						
Vacation								

🦴 DEBTS

	Budgeted	Remaining	Budgeted	Remaining	Budgeted	Remaining	Budgeted	Remaining
Car Payment 1	310	243						
Car Payment 2								
Credit Card 1 _____	150	93						
Credit Card 2 _____	45	48						
Credit Card 3 _____								
Credit Card 4 _____								
Credit Card 5 _____								
Student Loan 1								
Student Loan 2								
Student Loan 3								
Student Loan 4								
Other _Hospital_	48	0						
Other _____								
Other _____								
Other _____								
Other _____								
Other _____								
Other _____								
Other _____								
Other _____								
Other _____								
Other _____								
Other _____								
Other _____								

Irregular Income Planning

If you have an irregular income, this form just became your best friend!

Any additional irregular income goes here

Additional Irregular Income $\boxed{1,500}$

List, in priority order, anything that didn't make it in your monthly cash flow plan

Work back & forth, adding each budgeted item to the running total

ITEMS	BUDGETED	RUNNING TOTAL
Hospital Bill – Snowball	460	460
Home Depot – Snowball	770	1,230
Extra Entertainment	50	1,280
Chase Visa – Snowball	500	1,780
Extra Clothing	100	1,880

ONLINE BUDGETING RESOURCES

Dave recommends using a paper budget for the first few months, which is why we've included paper budget forms in the back of this workbook. Don't forget to check out additional in-depth budget tutorials when you sign in to the Military Toolkit at daveramsey.com/military/toolkit/signin.

GIVE YOUR BUDGET AN UPGRADE

If you're the point-and-click kind of Nerd, we have some great news! You can go from pen and paper to high tech by creating your free account with EveryDollar. You can access this through the Military Toolkit. Plan your personalized budget before the month begins and track it on the go. Access your EveryDollar budget at EveryDollar.com.

🕐 One-Minute Takeaway

What jumped out at you in this lesson? How can this affect your story?

_____

_____

_____

_____

_____

Small Group Discussion

True life-change happens when you open up and work through this material together. Break up into discussion groups of no more than 20 people to talk through the following questions. Be honest in your answers!

1 The key to true financial peace is to give every dollar a name by doing a fresh budget every single month. First, tell the group whether you're a Nerd or a Free Spirit. Then, share what you think about doing a zero-based budget every month from now on.

2 Dave stresses that you need to set aside a little "pocket money" to blow each month. Why is this important, and what kind of expenses would fall into this category?

3 Between cash, auto-drafts, debit cards and online transactions, we have a lot of different ways to spend money. How do all of these options impact your ability to actually "feel" money?

4 The envelope system is one of the best methods for learning how to feel money again. Using your Quick-Start Budget as a guide, discuss two or three areas for which you can try cash envelopes this month.

Breakout Group Exercise

Break into smaller groups of 4–5 people to work through the following activity. Choose a leader to read through the exercise aloud and keep the group on task. Your facilitator will call the groups back together to report your findings.

Case Study 1

Michael is a single service member who is in his third week of FPM, and he has not yet completed Baby Step 1. He has a monthly income of $1,000, but this activity will only deal with the portion of his budget shown below.

EXERCISE

As you can see, when Michael filled out his Monthly Cash Flow Plan, he was $100 under budget. In your breakout group, discuss what changes he could make and fill out the form on the right to get him to a zero balance.

Left to Budget: **800**

🐷 SAVING	Spent	Budgeted
Emergency Fund		0

🏠 HOUSING	Spent	Budgeted
First Mortgage/Rent		500

⚙ UTILITIES	Spent	Budgeted
Electricity		50
Gas		75
Water		25
Internet		50

Left to Budget: **800**

Total Budgeted: − **700**

Difference: = ZERO BALANCE **100**

Left to Budget: **800**

🐷 SAVING	Spent	Budgeted
Emergency Fund		

🏠 HOUSING	Spent	Budgeted
First Mortgage/Rent		

⚙ UTILITIES	Spent	Budgeted
Electricity		
Gas		
Water		
Internet		

Left to Budget: **800**

Total Budgeted: −

Difference: = ZERO BALANCE

You should end up at zero

Case Study 2

James and Kim have been married for nine years, and during that time, they've never lived on a budget. They have just started *Financial Peace Military*, and they're having a little trouble getting their first zero-based budget to balance. Your task is to help them out. James and Kim have a monthly income of $3,200, but this activity will only deal with the portion of their budget shown below.

EXERCISE

As you can see, when James and Kim filled out their Monthly Cash Flow Plan, they were $200 over budget. In your breakout group, discuss what changes they could make and fill out the form on the right to get them to a zero balance.

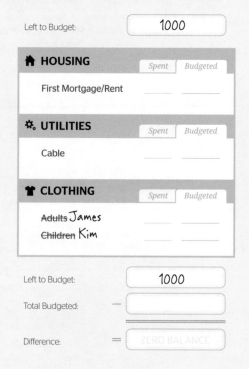

| Left to Budget: | 1000 | | Left to Budget: | 1000 |

🏠 HOUSING — Spent | Budgeted

| First Mortgage/Rent | | 850 |

⚙ UTILITIES — Spent | Budgeted

| Cable | | 150 |

👕 CLOTHING — Spent | Budgeted

| ~~Adults~~ James | | 100 |
| ~~Children~~ Kim | | 100 |

Left to Budget:	1000
Total Budgeted:	− 1200
Difference:	= ~~ZERO BALANCE~~ − 200

🏠 HOUSING — Spent | Budgeted

| First Mortgage/Rent | | |

⚙ UTILITIES — Spent | Budgeted

| Cable | | |

👕 CLOTHING — Spent | Budgeted

| ~~Adults~~ James | | |
| ~~Children~~ Kim | | |

Left to Budget:	1000
Total Budgeted:	−
Difference:	= ZERO BALANCE

Case Study 3

Chris and Sarah are newlyweds who received FPM as a wedding gift. They used wedding gift money to complete Baby Step 1, and they are paying off their last debt on Baby Step 2—a $5,000 car loan with a $400 monthly payment. Chris and Sarah have a monthly take-home pay of $3,500, but this activity will only deal with the portion of their budget shown below.

EXERCISE

Your goal is to help Chris and Sarah adjust their budget so they can pay extra on their car debt. There's no single right answer, so use Dave's principles to determine what you think Chris and Sarah should do.

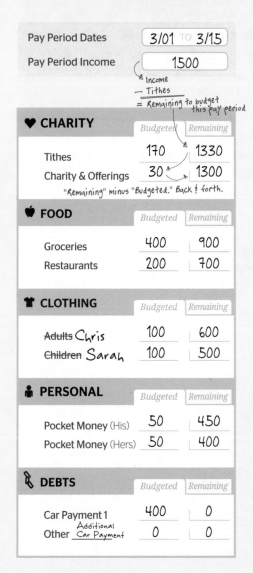

| Pay Period Dates | 3/01 TO 3/15 |
| Pay Period Income | 1500 |

↳ Income
— Tithes
‾‾‾‾‾‾
= Remaining to budget this pay period

♥ CHARITY	Budgeted	Remaining
Tithes	170	1330
Charity & Offerings	30	1300

"Remaining" minus "Budgeted." Back & forth.

🍎 FOOD	Budgeted	Remaining
Groceries	400	900
Restaurants	200	700

👕 CLOTHING	Budgeted	Remaining
~~Adults~~ Chris	100	600
~~Children~~ Sarah	100	500

👤 PERSONAL	Budgeted	Remaining
Pocket Money (His)	50	450
Pocket Money (Hers)	50	400

🔑 DEBTS	Budgeted	Remaining
Car Payment 1	400	0
Other _Additional Car Payment_	0	0

| Pay Period Dates | 3/01 TO 3/15 |
| Pay Period Income | 1500 |

↳ Income
— Tithes
‾‾‾‾‾‾
= Remaining to budget this pay period

♥ CHARITY	Budgeted	Remaining
Tithes	170	1330
Charity & Offerings	30	1300

"Remaining" minus "Budgeted." Back & forth.

🍎 FOOD	Budgeted	Remaining
Groceries		
Restaurants		

👕 CLOTHING	Budgeted	Remaining
~~Adults~~ Chris		
~~Children~~ Sarah		

👤 PERSONAL	Budgeted	Remaining
Pocket Money (His)		
Pocket Money (Hers)		

🔑 DEBTS	Budgeted	Remaining
Car Payment 1	400	
Other _Additional Car Payment_		

You should end up at zero

This Week's Homework

Personal finance is 20% head knowledge and 80% behavior. Take charge of your financial behaviors by completing the following tasks this week. Be sure to work with your spouse or accountability partner where noted!

☑ **Complete your first Monthly Cash Flow Plan.**
Use the paper form at the end of this workbook, download a printable copy from the Military Toolkit, or create a free EveryDollar account to complete your first zero-based budget. Be sure to bring it to class next week for your facilitator to review! Watch the tutorials online for more detailed help.

☑ **Call a Budget Committee Meeting.**
Singles: Share your zero-based budget with your accountability partner. Identify and discuss any parts of your budget that seem too expensive or out of control.

Married Couples: Call a Budget Committee Meeting and follow the rules outlined last week. Identify and discuss any parts of your budget that seem too expensive or out of control.

☑ **Stuff some envelopes.**
It's time to feel some money! Choose a few budget categories that would work well with the cash envelope system. Use the envelope icon on the budget forms for our suggestions.

You Know You're on a Budget When ...

Being on a budget doesn't mean you can't have fun! We asked Dave's Facebook fans for some clear signs that you might be on a budget.

Kristen: Your 4-year-old asks, "Mommy, do we have a coupon for this?" about any item she wants to buy in the grocery store!

Carrie: When you find yourself saying, "Dave would not want me to buy that!" and then walking away.

Travis: Your kids are constantly ticked off at Dave Ramsey!

Kirsten: School supplies become birthday presents.

Jeff: You have all the local supermarket ads spread out on the kitchen table, and you begin to strategize your coupons like you're about to invade Normandy.

Micki: You get one leg waxed at a time.

Natalie: You ask yourself, *How many shifts will I have to work to pay for this?*

Jondelyn: You search on the internet for recipes with ingredients in your pantry.

Michelle: When you're shopping with the kids, the 3-year-old asks for something, and the 7-year-old tells him, "It's not in the budget!"

Will: When you notice George Washington squint at the sunlight when you pull a dollar out of your wallet.

Ashlee: When your 5-year-old asks, "What is a mall?"

Gary: When you don't go out and spend money on Friday night and instead stay in and list stuff to sell on eBay.

Tell Your Story

Week 4

How would it feel to be 100% debt-free—
now and forever?

_____

_____

_____

_____

_____

_____

_____

_____

_____

_____

_____

_____

_____

DATE

DUMPING
DEBT

BREAKING THE CHAINS OF DEBT

Debt is the most successfully, aggressively marketed product in history. What? Debt isn't a product, is it? You bet it is. And it isn't just sold by banks and credit card companies anymore. Many national retail chains make more money on the sale of credit applications than they do on the actual merchandise they sell.

In *Dumping Debt*, Dave blows the lid off the credit game, debunking the leading myths about debt that have become ingrained in our natural way of thinking. Then he walks you right out of debt with his simple, clear and effective debt snowball technique.

Debunking the Myth

If you tell a lie or spread a _____ often enough, loud enough and long enough, the myth becomes accepted as _____.

Debt has been _____ to us in so many forms and so aggressively since the 1960s that to even imagine living without it requires a complete _____ _____.

The rich rule over the poor, and the borrower is slave to the lender.

—PROVERBS 22:7 (NIV)

Credit Card Myths

MYTH: You need a credit card to _____ a car or make _____ online.

TRUTH: A _____ card will do all of that.

MYTH: "I pay mine off every _____ with no annual fee. I get brownie points, air miles and a free hat."

TRUTH: More than 100 million Americans do _____ pay off the balance every month.

TRUTH: When you use plastic instead of cash, you spend more because you don't _____ it.

MYTH: "I'll make sure my _____ gets a credit card so he/she can learn to be responsible with money."

TRUTH: Teens are a huge _____ of credit card companies today.

Any money you owe to anyone for anything is debt. That includes credit cards, student loans and car loans!

I figured out that credit cards are not for emergencies. That's what I have savings for. DUH!

—Jennifer

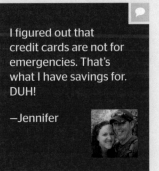

Car Myths

MYTH: Car _____ are a way of life, and you'll always have one.

TRUTH: The typical millionaire stays away from car payments by driving reliable used cars. That is _____ they became millionaires.

MYTH: _____ your car is what sophisticated financial people do. You should always lease things that go down in value. There are tax advantages.

TRUTH: *Consumer Reports, SmartMoney* magazine and a good calculator will tell you that the car lease is the most _____ way to finance and operate a vehicle.

MYTH: You can get a good deal on a _____ car.

TRUTH: A new car loses about _____% of its value in the first four years. This is the largest purchase most consumers make that goes down in value.

If you do rich people stuff, you get rich. If you do poor people stuff, you get poor.

Guidelines for All Vehicles:

1. The combined value of all your cars, motorcycles, boats and other vehicles should not be more than half your annual income—even if they're all paid for. If it is more than that, you have too much money tied up in things that go down in value.

2. If you can't pay off the car and all your other debts within two years, you should sell the car. You don't have room for it in your plan.

Lending Myths

MYTH: The home equity loan is _____ for consolidation and is a substitute for an emergency fund.

TRUTH: You don't go into _____ for emergencies.

MYTH: Debt consolidation _____ interest and you get just one smaller payment.

TRUTH: Debt consolidation typically saves little to no interest because you will throw your low-interest loans into the deal.

TRUTH: You can't borrow your way out of debt.

TRUTH: Smaller payments equal more time in debt.

TRUTH: Debt consolidation is a _____.

MYTH: By _____ a loan, you are helping out a friend or relative.

TRUTH: The bank requires a cosigner because the person isn't likely to _____. So be ready to pay the loan and have your credit damaged because you are on the loan.

Owe no one anything except to love one another.

—ROMANS 13:8

It's stupid to guarantee someone else's loan.

—PROVERBS 17:18 (CEV)

Credit Score Myth

MYTH: You need to take out a credit card or car loan
to "build up your _____ _____."

TRUTH: The FICO score is an "I love _____" score
and is not a measure of winning financially.

FICO BREAKDOWN

35% PAYMENT HISTORY
30% DEBT LEVEL
15% LENGTH OF HISTORY
10% NEW CREDIT
10% TYPE OF CREDIT

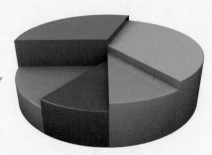

The Biggest Myth of All

MYTH: Debt is a _____and should be used to
create prosperity.

TRUTH: Debt is proof that the borrower is _____
to the lender.

TRUTH: When surveyed, the Forbes 400 were asked,
"What is the most important key to building
wealth?" _____% replied that becoming and
staying debt-free was the number-one key to
wealth building.

Gazelle Intensity

"My son, if you have become surety for your friend, if you have shaken hands in pledge for a stranger, you are snared by the words of your mouth; you are taken by the words of your mouth.

So do this, my son, and deliver yourself; for you have come into the hand of your friend: go and humble yourself; plead with your friend.

Give no sleep to your eyes, nor slumber to your eyelids.

Deliver yourself like a gazelle from the hand of the hunter, and like a bird from the hand of the fowler."

—Proverbs 6:1-5

How much could you _____, invest, blow, and _____ if you had no payments?

Steps Out of Debt

- Stop _____ more _____!

- You must _____ money.

- _____ something.

- Get a part-time _____ or overtime.

- _____ really works.

BABY STEP 2

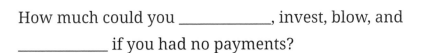

Pay off all debt using the _____ _____.

If you cannot afford the minimum payments on your debts, check out the online tutorial for the Pro Rata Debt List form immediately!

If you're currently in collections or facing bankruptcy, watch the free "Credit Sharks in Suits" lesson online immediately! You can find it in online in the Military Toolkit.

Debt Snowball

Get the ball rolling and start attacking your debt!

List your debts smallest to largest by balance

Once a debt is paid off, add the next minimum payment to your current amount. This becomes the new payment.

DEBTS	TOTAL PAYOFF	MIN. PAYMENT	NEW PAYMENT
Diagnostic	50	10	+ (Garage Sale)
Hospital Bill	460	38	= 48
Home Depot	770	45	93
Chase VISA	3,300	150	243
Car Loan	6,400	310	553

HAVING A FINANCIAL EMERGENCY?

If you cannot afford even the minimum payments on your debts, or if you are considering bankruptcy or facing pressure from debt collectors, do not lose hope! We have a free bonus lesson just for you!

In "Credit Sharks in Suits," Dave shows you how to handle calls from collectors while teaching you what your rights are under the law. He also unpacks the bankruptcy and post-bankruptcy process and shows you how to use the Pro Rata Debt List form.

One-Minute Takeaway

What jumped out at you in this lesson? How can this affect your story?

_____

_____

_____

_____

_____

Small Group Discussion

True life-change happens when you open up and work through this material together. Break up into discussion groups of no more than 20 people to talk through the following questions. Be honest in your answers!

1 Proverbs 22:7 says the borrower is the slave of the lender. What would your life look like right now if you were totally free with no debt whatsoever? What would you be able to do?

2 If you have any credit or debit cards in your purse or wallet, take a moment to get them out right now. While holding them in your hands, talk about the difference between these two types of cards.

This Week's Homework

Personal finance is 20% head knowledge and 80% behavior. Take charge of your financial behaviors by completing the following tasks this week. Be sure to work with your spouse or accountability partner where noted!

☑ **Complete the Debt Snowball form.**
Use either the online budget software or the paper form to list your debt snowball.

☑ **Discuss your Debt Snowball form.**
Singles: Share your Debt Snowball form with your accountability partner and discuss how long it will take for you to become debt-free. Brainstorm ways you can knock out the debt even faster. Review your budget to find ways to cut your spending and free up even more cash for your snowball.

Married Couples: Call a Budget Committee Meeting to review the Debt Snowball form and discuss how long it will take for you to become debt-free. Brainstorm ways you can knock out the debt even faster. Review your budget to find ways to cut your spending to free up even more cash for your snowball.

☑ **Chop some plastic.**
Even if you didn't cut up your credit cards in class, there's no reason why you can't do it right now! If you aren't ready to cut them up, meet with your accountability partner or spouse and discuss why you originally applied for them and why you've decided to keep them. If you cut up any credit cards that have a zero balance, be sure to call and close the account.

☐ **Extra Credit**: Watch the "Credit Sharks in Suits" lesson online on the Military Toolkit.

The Top 5 Debt Snowball Questions

It's the Baby Step that Dave is best known for: Baby Step 2, where you use the debt snowball to give your debt the beatdown.

BUT WAIT, YOU MAY SAY. What if I'm investing for retirement? Do I need to stop that? How do I know if I should sell one of my cars? People have a lot of questions when they start their debt snowball, but don't worry. We've got you covered with our top five.

1 Why pay the smallest debt first, instead of the one with the highest interest rate?

The point of the debt snowball is behavior modification. If you put a student loan first because it's got the highest interest rate, you won't see it leave for a while. You'll see numbers going down on a page, but that's it. Pretty soon,

you'll lose steam and stop paying extra, but you'll still have all your debts hanging around.

But when you ditch the small debt first, you see progress. That one debt is out of your life forever. Soon the second debt will follow, and then the next. When you see that the plan is working, you'll stick to it. By sticking to it, you'll eventually succeed in becoming debt-free!

2 How do I know when to sell something or pay it off?

A general rule of thumb is this: If it will take you more than 18-24 months to be debt-free on an

item, sell it. If you are making $500 monthly payments on your car and it will be another three years before it's paid off, get rid of it. The impact of freeing up that monthly payment, plus not owing a huge car balance, will rock your world.

The same rule goes for boats, rental properties and anything else except your home. Being free of the payment will drastically help your mindset and your wallet as you break the chains of debt. But if you own a motorcycle that will be paid off in a few months, it's all right to keep it. Just get rid of the debt on it!

3 Should I keep saving for retirement while in Baby Step 2?

No. You want to commit all your energy and resources to getting out of debt while on Baby Step 2, and diverting money toward retirement savings means you'll stay in debt longer. Don't dilute your efforts; concentrate on one thing at a time.

Even if you get a company match, don't take it while you're eliminating your debts. With a cut lifestyle, extra income from a second job (if you take one) and extreme focus, you'll get out of debt quickly and establish your full emergency fund. Then you can go right back to investing. Being debt-free will more than make up for taking a year or two off of investing.

5 What if I get laid off while paying off?

That's scary to think about, but if you lose your job, go into survival mode.

"When you see that the plan is working, you'll stick to it. By sticking to it, you'll eventually succeed in becoming debt-free!"

4 What if a baby is on the way?

First off, congratulations! A baby is always cause for celebration. What you want to do if you're expecting is to stop the debt snowball and pile up cash. Keep making your minimum payments, but stock away all the

remaining money. If an emergency happens and there are medical bills, then you have the money there to take care of them.

Once your new bundle of joy is home and everyone is all right, then take your saved-up money and apply it to the debt snowball.

Make sure your lifestyle is slashed to the basics. Keep up your minimum payments, but no extra ones. Stop the debt snowball until you find work (and get a job delivering pizzas or some other work until you land a full-time position with another company).

If you get severance pay, don't kick back and live off of that. Try not to even touch it. Live bare bones and hunt like crazy for work. The sooner you get a new job, the sooner that severance looks like a huge bonus that you can apply toward the debt snowball.

If your church has a coaching ministry, reach out for help with your debt and budgeting questions.

Tell Your Story

Week 5

What's your current process for planning for and making major purchases?

_____

_____

_____

_____

_____

_____

_____

_____

_____

_____

_____

_____

_____
DATE

BUYER
BEWARE

THE POWER OF MARKETING ON YOUR BUYING DECISIONS

Can you recite, from memory, the advertising slogans of at least 10 companies? Have you ever experienced buyer's remorse? America is the most marketed-to country on Earth. Thousands of companies are clamoring for our money—and we usually run to hand it to them!

In *Buyer Beware*, Dave draws on years of selling and marketing experience to show you exactly how all of these businesses get their message deep into your subconscious. Then, once you understand the game, Dave and Jon will show you how to finally gain power over your purchases and get the best deal when you're ready to buy.

The goal of every business is to make a profit. If they don't, they close.

The plans of the diligent lead surely to plenty, but those of everyone who is hasty, surely to poverty.

—PROVERBS 21:5

The Rule of 78 is a method of calculating the total interest on certain types of loans. Under the Rule of 78, earlier payments are weighted with more interest than later ones. As such, paying off the loan early results in you paying more in interest.

Caveat Emptor

Let the Buyer Beware!

Companies use every angle to aggressively compete for your _____.

Major Ways Companies Market to Us

- _____ selling

- _____ and _____ payment methods as a marketing tool

    - ____% of the 90-days-same-as-cash contracts convert to payments that are usually at _____% APR with the Rule of 78 prepayment penalty

    - Convenient Payment Methods:
        - > Store loyalty and reward cards
        - > Store debit and credit cards
        - > Mobile payment options

- _____, radio, magazines, _____ and other media

  - TV ads are incredibly expensive. A typical 30-second national TV commercial costs nearly $300,000 to produce—that's $_____ per second!

  - By contrast, the cost to produce an entire hour of prime-time public television is about the same—$300,000, which comes to $_____ per second.

- Product _____

  - Brand Recognition
  - Color
  - Shelf Position and Packaging

Significant Purchases

A "significant purchase" is normally anything over $_____.

Our bodies go through physiological _____ when making a significant purchase.

We all have that spoiled, red-faced, grocery store kid living inside of us. His name is _____.

For where your treasure is, there your heart will be also.

—MATTHEW 6:21

In order to have financial peace, sometimes you have to look in the mirror and say, "No, not today."

Gaining Power Over Purchase

Because you can always spend more than you make, you must develop power over purchase.

He who is impulsive exalts folly.

—PROVERBS 14:29

STRATEGIES FOR WISE BUYING DECISIONS

- Wait _____ before making a purchase.

- Carefully consider your buying _____.
  No amount of _____ equals contentment or fulfillment.

- Never buy anything that you do not
  _____.

- Consider the "_____ _____" of your money.

- Seek the _____ of your spouse.

You don't want to keep up with the Joneses. They're broke.

> *Who can find a virtuous wife? For her worth is far above rubies. The heart of her husband safely trusts her; so he will have no lack of gain.*
>
> —PROVERBS 31:10–11

"Let the buyer beware" means I am responsible for my own foolish purchases.

—Julie

Simple Rules for Successful Negotiating

- Always tell the absolute _____.

- Use the power of _____.

- Understand and use _____-_____ power.

- Learn to _____ _____.

- Say, "That's not _____ _____!"

- Identify the dreaded _____ guy, _____ guy technique.

- Master the "If I _____ _____" technique.

BONUS VIDEO

For more tips on how to get the best bargain every time, be sure to check out the free bonus lesson, *That's Not Good Enough.*

daveramsey.com/military/toolkit/signin

One-Minute Takeaway

What jumped out at you in this lesson? How can this affect your story?

_____

_____

_____

_____

_____

Small Group Discussion

True life-change happens when you open up and work through this material together. Break up into discussion groups of no more than 20 people to talk through the following questions. Be honest in your answers!

1 Now that the tactics are fresh on your mind, we want to make sure your new budget doesn't get wrecked by a clever marketing campaign. What brand's commercials, ads or marketing do you find most compelling? Why do you think they are so effective on you?

2 What was the last thing that caused that red-faced grocery store kid inside of you to wake up and scream, "I want one!"? Did you give in to the urge to buy?

3 Proverbs 1:5 says, "A wise man will hear and increase learning, and a man of understanding will attain wise counsel." What are some ways you can attain wise counsel before making a major purchase?

4 It's now been two weeks since you did your first zero-based budget. We know this can take some getting used to, so what questions do you have about your budget?

5 Pull out your Monthly Cash Flow Plan form or your budget from EveryDollar. Have you identified any areas that have been particular trouble spots for you in the past? In what areas do you feel you might be overspending?

This Week's Homework

Personal finance is 20% head knowledge and 80% behavior. Take charge of your financial behaviors by completing the following tasks this week. Be sure to work with your spouse or accountability partner where noted!

☑ **Define "major purchase."**
What would make up a "major purchase" in your world? Singles, run this by your accountability partner to get their feedback. Married couples, commit to not make a major purchase without following the rules outlined in this lesson.

☑ **Discuss your zero-based budget.**
Singles: Talk to your accountability partner about how easy or difficult it has been to live on your zero-based budget the past two weeks.

Married Couples: Call a quick Budget Committee Meeting and discuss how easy or difficult it has been to live on your zero-based budget the past two weeks. Are there any adjustments that need to be made? If so, be sure to make the changes together as a team!

☑ **Do a marketing self-assessment.**
Look around your home and pay attention to the kinds of things you normally purchase. What marketing techniques are working on you? What do you regret buying? What purchases have you truly enjoyed? Making a mental note of these things will really help your buying decisions in the future.

☐ **Extra Credit**: Watch the free one-hour lesson of *That's Not Good Enough* online on the Military Toolkit.

7 Things You Don't (Really) Need

*Do you know the difference between your **needs** and your **wants?***

EVERY DAY, the marketing world tells you that you *need* this or you *need* that. The hype machine never stops turning. But you would be amazed at the number of things you don't actually need, things you won't realize you don't need until you're forced to go without them.

If you can get to the point where you can see through the marketing hype, you'll begin to realize that a lot of your *needs* are simply *wants.*

To help you get started, here's a list of some common things that you can live without while getting out of debt.

1 Cut the cable.
A normal cable bill can approach $100 a month after all the special introductory rates have expired. Don't get sucked into the three-month specials, because when those wear off, you'll find yourself paying a hefty cable bill to watch shows you can probably

"What are some things you are currently spending money on that you don't really need?"

watch online anyway. Television is not a necessity. It's a luxury. Besides, you can probably get all the local channels in your area—

many in HD—with a set of rabbit-ear antennas.

2 Ditch private schools.
This should really go without saying, but too many people think it's just a fact of life to put their kid through an elementary school that's more expensive

than college. How does that make sense? Don't buy into the hype of keeping up with the Joneses or thinking your kid will be a deadbeat if he goes to public school. Use that money to get out of debt, then start saving for college.

3 Take a break from vacation.
No! Not vacation! Yes. Vacation. The brochures are so pretty. The websites are so descriptive. And, after all, don't you deserve a vacation? Yes, you do . . . when you're out of debt. You can take a couple of years off from lounging in the sand while you get your financial life in order. The beach isn't going anywhere. Plus, you can always make plans for some cheap getaways or even have a "staycation!"

4 Stop eating out.
The more kids you have, the more expensive it gets to eat out. Multiply that by a couple of times a week, and you can spend a crazy amount of money on restaurants each month. But here's the thing: Grocery stores have food too! And if you plan ahead (which is part of budgeting), then you buy exactly what you need. Plus, you aren't left scrambling to make dinner plans at 5:30 every evening.

5 Give up the gadgets.
The newest digital tablet. The newest smartphone. The newest, biggest television with optional

laser beam attachment. Are these really things that you must have, considering that, just a few years ago, no one had them? Take a breath. Your goal is to get out of debt, not to get the newest toys every month.

6 Quit buying the hottest name-brand new clothes.
You might be shocked at how many people go into thousands of dollars of debt because of an addiction to buying shoes, purses or suits. This goes for

both men and women. You don't have to look like a fashion magazine cover model while you are getting out of debt. Make do with what you have until you're in a better situation with your money.

7 Sacrifice the expensive hobbies.
Is it really necessary to spend $200 a month on golf while you still have $20,000 in credit card debt? Or a couple hundred a month on yoga lessons? Really? You still need hobbies—so don't cut those out of your life, even golf—but keep them in check. Budget for it and only spend your hard-earned cash on hobbies that you can afford.

Now that's just a short list of stuff. This list could probably fill up pages of your workbook. Really, it's just about you taking an honest inventory of your financial life and figuring out what you can live without—just for a little while.

So think about your own life. What are some things you are currently spending money on that you don't really need?

KEY TERMS

Brand Recognition: Consumer awareness about a particular brand; generally tied to specific marketing techniques

Buyer's Remorse: Feeling of regret about a purchase soon after making it

Caveat Emptor: Latin term meaning "let the buyer beware"

Financing: Purchasing an item using debt; attractive terms and conditions often used as a marketing technique

Impulse Purchase: An item that is purchased without any consideration of the long-term effects

Markup: The difference between the wholesale price and retail price

Negotiating: Act of bargaining for a lower price

Walk-Away Power: The emotional distance a buyer has from the item; refers to the ability to walk away from a purchase if a good price cannot be reached through negotiation

Tell Your Story

Week 6

What insurance policies do you currently carry? How and why did you select them?

_____

_____

_____

_____

_____

_____

_____

_____

_____

_____

_____

_____

_____

_____

_____

DATE

THE ROLE OF INSURANCE

PROTECTING YOUR HEALTH, FAMILY AND FINANCES

Insurance? Yikes! This is a topic that few people really enjoy, and yet it is an area that impacts your finances more than you could possibly imagine! Can you explain how your life insurance works? If your spouse were suddenly widowed, how much would he or she need to survive? How does health insurance work? Are specialty plans, such as cancer policies, a good deal? Let's find out!

In *The Role of Insurance*, Dave walks you through the seven types of insurance that every adult needs, and he reveals how to avoid the traps in the insurance industry that can leave you—and your heirs—flat broke!

Understanding Insurance

The purpose of insurance is to _____HANDLE_____ risk.

Without proper insurance, certain losses can

_____ you.

Basic Types of Insurance:

- Homeowner's or Renter's
- Auto
- Health
- Disability
- Long-Term Care
- Identity Theft Protection
- Life

Auto Insurance

If you have a full emergency fund, raise your

DEDUCTIBLE.

Carry adequate _____.

Consider dropping your _____ on older cars.

Look at your auto insurance policy to see how much liability you currently carry. It often looks like this: 100/300/100.

Homeowner's and Renter's

Homeowner's coverage should be guaranteed
_____ cost if at all possible.

If you're in an apartment or other rental arrangement,
you need _RENTERS_____ insurance.

An _____ liability policy is a good buy
once you begin building wealth.

Health Insurance

Increase your _DEDUCTIBLE___ and/or
coinsurance amount to bring premiums down.

Increase your _____-_____ but never
decrease the _____ pay.

Decreasing *either* of these to save on premium costs is
a horrible idea. You would take on way too much risk!

See if an _____—a Health Savings Account—would
make sense for your specific situation.

The HSA is a _____-_____ savings
account for medical expenses that works with a high-
deductible insurance policy.

Extended Replacement Cost has become more common with the big-name insurance companies. However, Extended may not pay enough to actually replace your home and possessions. Always know exactly what the maximum benefit is in relation to the value of your home.

With an HSA, you're paying the medical bills with your own money. This makes you a wiser and more careful medical consumer.

HSA BENEFITS INCLUDE:

- Deposits are 100% tax-deductible.

- You can save up to 100% of your deductible in the savings account.

- You can pay most medical expenses with tax-free dollars.

- Unused money stays in the account and grows interest on a tax-favored basis to supplement retirement, just like an IRA.

Disability Insurance

Disability insurance is designed to replace _____ lost due to a short-term or permanent disability.

Try to buy disability insurance that pays if you cannot perform the job that you were educated or _____ to do.

That is called _____, or "own occ," disability. Many times, this is only available for two years.

Beware of _____-term policies covering less than five years.

Always buy long-term disability insurance with after-tax dollars. This way, disability benefits will be tax-free.

If your company provides a long-term disability insurance option alongside your company health care plan, you should buy it. It will almost always be cheaper that way than you'll find on the open market.

Your coverage should be for _____% of your current income.

A _____ elimination period will _____ your premium cost.

The _____ period is the time between being declared disabled and when the payments actually begin.

Long-Term Care Insurance

Long-term care insurance is for _____ home, assisted living facilities and in-home care.

This is a must-have for anyone _____ years old or older.

Among people turning 65 today, 69% will need some form of long-term care!

Identity Theft Protection

Don't buy ID theft protection that only provides credit report _____.

_____ protection includes restoration services that assign a counselor to clean up the mess.

Life Insurance

Life insurance is to replace lost income due to _____.

Most people have no _____ what kind of life insurance they _____.

TWO TYPES OF LIFE INSURANCE:

- _TERM LIFE_ insurance is for a specified period, is substantially cheaper, and has no savings plan built into it. ~~CASH~~ ~~VALUE~~
- ~~TERM~~ ~~LIFE~~ insurance is normally for life and is more expensive in order to fund a savings plan.

The most common insurance myth is that the need for life insurance is a _____ situation.

Twenty years from now, with the kids grown and gone, when you're debt-free (including that 15-year mortgage) and you have substantial investments, you have become _____-insured. Your need for life insurance has gone away.

The BIG Question About

LIFE INSURANCE

Joe is age 30 and spends $178 on life insurance each month. What is the best way to spend his money?

BAD

| Insurance | $178 MONTHLY |
| Investments | ? MONTHLY |

INSURANCE
$250,000
in Whole Life

BETTER

| Insurance | $13 MONTHLY |
| Investments | $165 MONTHLY |

INSURANCE
$250,000
in 20-Year Term

BEST

| Insurance | $21 MONTHLY |
| Investments | $157 MONTHLY |

INSURANCE
$500,000
in 20-Year Term

CASH VALUES

| AT AGE 50 | $34,483 | AT AGE 50 | $164,859 | AT AGE 50 | $156,866 |
| AT AGE 70 | $124,041 | AT AGE 70 | $1,960,603 | AT AGE 70 | $1,865,539 |

Insurance cost and cash value based on the average of four actual quotes. Investments assume a 12% rate of return.

The bottom line should be perfectly clear:

Buy term and invest the rest!

Why Not Use Life Insurance for Investing?

Returns are historically _____.

When you die with cash value, the insurance company _____ the cash value.

The _____ deducted from your return are extremely _____.

Life Insurance: What to Buy

You need about _____ times your income. Invested at a 10–12% rate of return, the growth would replace your lost income.

Don't forget your _____.

Children only need enough for _____ expenses.

Make sure you have a new policy in place _____ you cancel any existing cash value policies!

Insurance to Avoid

- _____ life and disability

- _____ and hospital indemnity

- Accidental _____

Don't try to do any wealth building inside an insurance policy. It just doesn't work.

A stay-at-home mom brings enormous economic value to the home. If something were to happen to her, dad would need the money to replace part of what mom does.

Insurance can be an intimidating, confusing mess if you don't know what you're doing. Be sure to work only with a qualified professional with the heart of a teacher.

_____.

- Pre-paid _____ policies

- _____ life insurance

- Policies with fancy _____
  - Return of premium
  - Waiver of premium

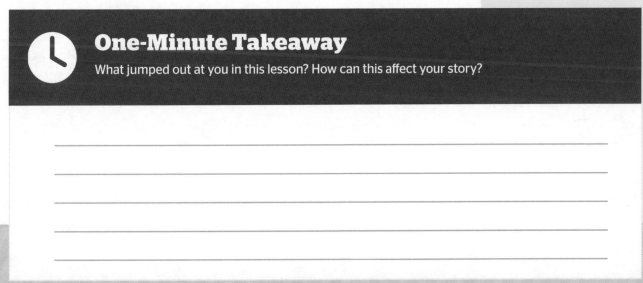

One-Minute Takeaway

What jumped out at you in this lesson? How can this affect your story?

_____

_____

_____

_____

_____

Small Group Discussion

True life-change happens when you open up and work through this material together. Break up into discussion groups of no more than 20 people to talk through the following questions. Be honest in your answers!

1 We just watched a powerful, sobering story about why having the right kind of life insurance is so important. Take a few minutes to respond to the Steve Maness story. What, if anything, does this inspire you to do regarding your own insurance plans?

2 Having the correct types of insurance is vital to the physical and emotional health of your family. What would happen to you and your family if a catastrophic event happened and you had no or insufficient insurance coverage in one of the key areas of insurance?

Breakout Group Exercise

Break into smaller groups of 4-5 people to work through the following activity. Choose a leader to read through the exercise aloud and keep the group on task. Your facilitator will call the groups back together to report your findings.

Case Study 1

Corey is a service member who needs help figuring out which insurance policies he needs. He lives in a two-bedroom apartment with his wife, Laura, who is currently not working as she finishes up school. The couple lives on Corey's $41,000 salary, they are debt-free, and they share one car.

Corey already has the following policies in place:

🛡 *Renter's Insurance*

🛡 *Auto Insurance*

🛡 *Cancer Insurance*

Discuss which policies Corey and Laura should keep, cancel and add:

POLICIES TO KEEP	POLICIES TO CANCEL	POLICIES TO ADD
_____	_____	_____
_____	_____	_____
_____	_____	_____
_____	_____	_____
_____	_____	_____

Case Study 2

Vickie has been driving for 12 years without any major auto accidents—until today. It was pouring rain when she left the office, and within minutes of leaving she was forced to make an evasive maneuver that caused her to go into a spin on the wet road. After knocking an expensive, high-end luxury car down an embankment, Vickie came to a stop by smashing into the side of a mid-range sedan.

She was found to be at fault in the accident, so let's look at the extent of the damage she caused:

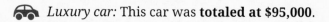 *Luxury car:* This car was **totaled at $95,000**.

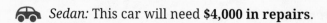 *Sedan:* This car will need **$4,000 in repairs**.

Hospital bills: The driver of the luxury car had $15,000 in medical bills for a broken arm, while his passenger had **$185,000 in medical bills** for emergency surgery and recovery.

Like many Americans, Vickie carries a 100/300/100 liability policy. Here's a basic look at what that covers:

make sure you catch this.

100/300/100
① ② ③

1. **Bodily Injury Per Person**
The most your insurance will pay (in thousands of dollars) for any injuries you cause **per person.**

2. **Bodily Injury Per Accident**
The maximum combined amount (in thousands of dollars) your insurance will pay for any injuries you cause **per accident.**

3. **Property Damage**
The most your insurance will pay (in thousands of dollars) to repair or replace any **vehicles or objects** you damage during an accident.

DISCUSSION QUESTIONS

1. Using the summary of the accident, calculate the total dollar value of the **property damage** Vickie caused.

    > TOTAL

2. Does she have enough coverage to cover the damages?   ○ Yes   ○ No

3. How much **per person and per accident** will Vickie's insurance pay for **bodily injury** that she caused?

    Bodily Injury Per Person: > TOTAL

    Bodily Injury Per Accident: > TOTAL

4. Given the fact that Vickie does not have an umbrella policy in place, **how much** of the remaining hospital bills for the **passenger in the luxury car** will she be held personally responsible for?

    > TOTAL

> *Did something in this case study make you question whether or not you have enough liability coverage? If you need to update your policy, do it immediately! Accidents never happen on schedule. Call your insurance agent and take care of this as soon as possible!*

Case Study 3

Bill and Katie want to save money on their monthly insurance expenses, but they're being careful not to make any big mistakes. They are both 32 years old and in great physical health, and each has a $50,000 income. The couple took FPM two years ago, and they're now totally debt-free with a fully funded emergency fund.

They have several insurance policies in place, but in this exercise, we'll only focus on these three:

🛡 *Life*: Bill and Katie each have a 20-year **$500,000 term life policy**.

🛡 *Health*: Each has a **PPO** plan with an **80/20 copay** and **$500 deductible**.

🛡 *Long-Term Care*: Bill has a 10-year policy with a 180-day elimination period.

DISCUSSION QUESTIONS

1. Bill is trying to convince Katie to lower their **term life policies** to $250,000, but Katie does not think the savings of $8 a month is worth it. Explain to your group who you think is right and why.

2. Because Bill and Katie are in such great health, they have considered dropping their **health insurance** altogether. Discuss how and why they could come to regret this decision.

3. Identify three wise things Bill and Katie could change in their **health insurance policy** that would lower their premium.

4. Is **long-term care insurance** a wise choice for Bill right now? Why or why not?

This Week's Homework

Personal finance is 20% head knowledge and 80% behavior. Take charge of your financial behaviors by completing the following tasks this week. Be sure to work with your spouse or accountability partner where noted!

☑ **Identify your insurance coverages.**
Use the Insurance Coverage Recap form in the back of the book or online to list the policies you currently have. Note any of Dave's recommended seven basic types of coverage that are missing from your list as well as any policies that you need to update or remove. Make sure your spouse or any dependents know where to find this form in the event of an emergency.

☑ **Discuss the Insurance Coverage Recap form.**
Singles: Review your Insurance Coverage Recap form with your accountability partner and discuss any changes you're considering making.

Married Couples: Review the Insurance Coverage Recap form together and discuss any changes that need to be made. Make sure you both know where to find the form in the event of an emergency.

☑ **Adjust your zero-based budget.**
If you changed or added any insurance policies as a result of this lesson, be sure to make the necessary updates to your monthly zero-based budget to account for any changes to your premiums.

A Bittersweet Victory

"Whereas you do not know what will happen tomorrow. For what is your life? It is even a vapor that appears for a little time and then vanishes away." —JAMES 4:14

AS SCRIPTURE SAYS, you are not guaranteed tomorrow. You know this is true, but it's so much easier to look the other way and pretend to be invincible. Sadly, reality can be a lot less pleasant than fantasy.

That's why Dave encourages everyone—both young and old—to purchase quality term life insurance. Wise adults and loving spouses realize if they wait until tragedy hits to make provisions for their family, they've waited far too long.

This small effort now may end up leaving a lasting impression on your loved ones, just like it did for Kirstie and her two daughters.

Before they were married, Kirstie and her husband, Brad, took *Financial Peace*. They walked through the Baby Steps, lived on less than they made, used the cash envelope system, and got a good life insurance policy.

> *"Wise adults and loving spouses realize if they wait until tragedy hits to make provisions for their family, they've waited far too long."*

A few years into their marriage, while proudly following both Dave's and her granny's advice, Kirstie was happy to find herself pregnant with their second child. Unfortunately, the joy of a growing family was soon overshadowed by devastating news: Brad was diagnosed with stage IV lung cancer. They fought the cancer for 13 months, but then Brad, 38, went to be with the Lord.

"Had we not had the foresight to live differently than the rest of America, we wouldn't have been able to plan as well as we did. We wouldn't be where we are, had we not taken your class and really listened," an emotional Kirstie told Dave when she called in to *The Dave Ramsey Show*.

Kirstie and Brad not only listened to the FPM principles, they were also inspired by other people's stories to take action. They each purchased a $250,000 life insurance policy, deciding this amount would more than cover the remaining balance on the house. If something happened to one of them, the grieving spouse wouldn't have to worry about this debt.

By working through Dave's process and applying God's ways of handling money, they tackled their debts together, with only the mortgage

> ## *"The simple task of getting life insurance is one of the most loving gifts you can ever give your family."*

remaining. When Brad lost his battle with cancer, Kirstie used the life insurance proceeds to pay off the house. "It's kind of a bittersweet victory," she said, "but it's honoring what our original plan was together."

As a couple, they were dedicated to achieving their FPM goals, including making insurance an important part of their financial plan. In total, they paid off $136,000. Because of their focus and determination, Kirstie is able to raise her daughters, Elizabeth and Sophia, with the financial peace of mind that only comes from being completely debt-free.

At the end of the call, Dave challenged his listeners: "If you don't have life insurance by the end of the day after

listening to that call, and you have a family, I think something's probably wrong with your brain."

It's the hearing *and the doing* that really count. The simple task of getting life insurance is one of the most loving gifts you can ever give your family. So do it!

It's extremely difficult, if not impossible, to get good term life insurance after you've been diagnosed with a serious, life-threatening illness. And the truth is, you could go from totally healthy to terminally ill in a single doctor's visit. Once you get the bad news, your chances of getting life insurance could be gone forever.

Brad left a legacy for Kirstie and their kids because he *bothered* to do this stuff. If you don't have quality life insurance, it's time to move this to the top of your family's to-do list today!

Tell Your Story

Week 7

How are today's financial decisions impacting the legacy you'll leave for your family?

_____

_____

_____

_____

_____

_____

_____

_____

_____

_____

_____

_____

_____

_____

_____
DATE

RETIREMENT
AND COLLEGE
PLANNING

MASTERING THE ALPHABET SOUP OF INVESTING

Just picture it: You're out of debt and you have an emergency fund of three to six months of expenses sitting in the bank. Now it's time to build some wealth for your future!

In *Retirement and College Planning*, Dave helps you understand all those initials and abbreviations: IRA, 401(k), 403(b), 457 and more! Plus, Rachel shows you the best way to make sure your kids get through college without a student loan—what an idea!

Let's Dream Together

IMAGINE IF...
A 30-year-old couple made $48,000 a year and saved 15% (**$600 per month**) in a 401(k) at 12% growth.

AT 70 YEARS OLD, THEY WILL HAVE...
$7,058,863 in the 401(k).

IMAGINE IF...
That same couple fully funded a Roth IRA at $5,000 each per year (a total of $10,000), which would be **$833 per month**, at 12% growth.

AT 70 YEARS OLD, THEY WILL HAVE...
$9,803,937—TAX FREE!

WHAT IF...
That same 30-year-old couple, DEBT FREE, does both?

AT 70 YEARS OLD, THEY WILL HAVE...

401(k)	$7,058,863
Roth IRA	$9,803,937
Total	**$16,862,800**

Ground Rules for Investing

Once the emergency fund is in place, you should begin retirement and college funding, which all fall within long-term investing for _____.

 Invest _____ % of your household income into Roth IRAs / Roth TSPs and pre-tax retirement plans.

Simple Investing

The KISS Rule of Investing:
Keep it _____, _____!

Diversification means to _____ _____.

Diversification _____ risk.

Give portions to seven, yes to eight, for you do not know what disaster may come upon the land.
—ECCLESIASTES 11:2 (NIV84)

Mutual Funds

Investors pool their _____ to invest.

Professional portfolio managers manage the pool or _____.

Your _____ comes as the _____ of the fund is increased.

Mutual funds are good _____-term investments.

Standard Diversification Plan

- 25% in _____ and _____ funds.

- 25% in _____ funds.

- 25% in _____ funds.

- 25% in Aggressive _____ funds.

Use Tax-Favored Plans

Always save long term with tax-_____ dollars.

Tax-favored means that the investment is in a _____ _____ or has special tax treatment.

QUALIFIED PLANS

- Individual Retirement Arrangement (IRA)
- 401(k)
- 403(b)
- 457
- Simplified Employee Pension Plan (SEP)

Individual Retirement Arrangement (IRA)

Remember, an IRA is not a type of _____ at a bank. It is the tax _____ on virtually any type of investment.

Everyone with an _____ income is eligible. Also, the non-income-producing spouse of an income earner is eligible.

Roth IRA

The Roth IRA is an _____-tax IRA that grows TAX _____!

If you _____ like we teach, you should use the Roth IRA.

> I'm in my forties and only have a 401(k). My takeaway is that I am WAY behind and need to get busy saving.
>
> —Michelle

Laws, regulations and eligibility requirements change all the time. That's why it's important to find a professional to help you navigate the investing waters.

> The Roth IRA is named for Senator William Roth (R-Delaware), who authored this section of the Taxpayer Relief Act of 1997.

401(k), 403(b) and 457 Retirement Plans

Most companies have completely done away with
traditional _____ plans in the last 20 years.
Some new plans offer a variety of pre-tax choices.

Some companies are now offering the _____
401(k), which grows tax free.

You should be funding your plan whether your company
_____ or not, but the plans that have
company matching provide great returns.

Rollovers

You should _____ roll all retirement plans to
an IRA when you _____ the company.

Do not bring the money home! Make it a _____
_____.

Retirement Loans

Never _____ on your retirement plan.

The Roth 401(k) is one of the only
tax—free investments for people
who don't meet the income limits
for a Roth IRA. If your company
offers one, take it.

WHY NOT?

- The interest you pay yourself is nowhere close to what you would be earning in the mutual fund if you hadn't unplugged that investment.

- You may leave the company before the loan is repaid. That means you would have to repay within 60 days and risk fees and extra taxes at a time when you may have lost your income.

- You may die before the loan is repaid, which would leave a mess for your heirs.

Our Suggestion for Investing 15%

- Fund a 401(k) or other employer plans if they match. Fund an amount equal to the _____.

- Above the match amount, fund _____ IRAs. If there is no match, start with Roth IRAs.

- Complete 15% of your income by going back to the _____ or other company plans.

> *Do you not know that in a race all the runners run, but only one gets the prize? Run in such a way as to get the prize.*
>
> —1 CORINTHIANS 9:24 (NIV)

If you're in the military or are a government employee, you probably have a Thrift Savings Account option available. Get Dave's suggestion on how to use your TSP online in the Military Toolkit.

College Funding

BABY STEP 5

Save for your children's
_____ *using tax-favored plans.*

Paying for College

First, save in an Education Savings Account (ESA), or "education _____."

Above that, if you want to save more, or if you don't meet the income limits for an ESA, use a certain type of _____ plan.

The only type of 529 we recommend is one that leaves _____ in control of the mutual fund at all times.

NEVER BUY A 529 PLAN THAT:

- _____ your options.

- Automatically changes your investments based on the _____ of the child.

Three Nevers of College Saving

- Never save for college using _____.

- Never save for college using _____ bonds.

- Never save for college using _____ tuition, which only covers the tuition inflation rate.

Debt-Free College

Is debt-free college even possible if you don't have a big college fund ready to go? Of course!

DEBT-FREE COLLEGE TIPS

- Pick an _____-_____ or _____ college.

- Compare _____-campus versus _____- campus living options.

- Aim for scholarships with SAT and ACT _____.

- Get a _____!

One-Minute Takeaway

What jumped out at you in this lesson? How can this affect your story?

_____

_____

_____

_____

_____

Small Group Discussion

True life-change happens when you open up and work through this material together. Break up into discussion groups of no more than 20 people to talk through the following questions. Be honest in your answers!

1 Winning with money is not just about building a comfortable retirement for yourself. It also includes leaving a legacy for future generations. Realistically, what type of inheritance would you like to leave your loved ones? What would you like to see them do with it?

2 Parents often struggle with the idea of putting their own retirement plans ahead of their children's college funding. Why is it so important to follow the Baby Steps in order in this area? Why do you think some parents feel compelled to reverse the order of these two steps?

3 Some people struggle with the concept of doing the Baby Steps in order, one step at a time, while setting aside or delaying goals they want to reach immediately. Why is it important to focus all your attention and gazelle intensity on one goal at a time?

This Week's Homework

☑ **Learn more about your retirement options.**
Your retirement may seem like it's a long way away, but it's important to start saving now so you'll be prepared when the time comes. Take some time this week to review your specific retirement options. The Department of Defense Military Compensation website and Military One Source website are great places to start. Your facilitator can help you find specific resources for your retirement benefits.

☑ **Think about your college savings needs.**
If you have kids or if you are planning on going to school yourself, take some time this week to think about how you will save for it.

☑ **Discuss your retirement plans.**
Singles: Meet with your accountability partner and discuss your retirement plans (and dreams). Review the calculations from the Monthly Retirement Planning exercise together.

Married Couples: Call a Budget Committee Meeting to discuss your retirement plans (and dreams). Commit to reach those goals as a team.

5 Top Questions Parents Ask About College Savings

College savings plans can limit how you use your money. Picking the right one can make a huge difference.

TODAY'S PARENTS believe they owe their children a full ride to college at all costs. While college is important, it does not rank above retirement or the emergency fund. And it is *not* a reason to go into debt.

Once you reach Baby Step 5 and it's time to start saving for college, you have several options. We recommend investing in good growth stock mutual funds and an Education Savings Account (ESA). The ESA turbo-charges your college savings with tax-free growth and withdrawals as long as you spend the money on education.

Flexible, state-sponsored 529 plans also let you save and use your college savings tax free and can be a good choice in the right situation. Here are a few questions to help you understand the role each one can play in your college savings plan.

Q *How can I use the money?*
A Obviously, you're opening this account to pay for educational expenses, but each plan defines that differently. ESAs allow you to use the funds for private elementary, middle or high school tuition as well as post-secondary education. You can also pay for off-campus housing, computers and other education-related expenses with your ESA. But eligible expenses for a 529 plan are limited to college tuition, room and board, school-required books and supplies.

Q *How much can I invest?*
A If you plan to open your college fund with $2,000 or less, go with an ESA. You can contribute up to $2,000 per year per child in an ESA. If you want to save more, or if the child's parents make more than $200,000 per year, a 529 has no annual contribution limit or income restrictions. You can also open both, using the first $2,000 to start the ESA (if the parents meet the income requirements) and putting the rest into the 529. This is a good option if your child is planning on getting advanced degrees or attending medical or law school. Contribution limits and eligibility requirements are a moving target, so be sure to check our online resources for the most up-to-date information.

Q *How much control do I have?*

A Like a Roth IRA, you can invest in any mutual fund in any allocation you wish in your ESA—that's what makes an ESA a better option than the 529 for most people. You can also change funds as often as you want. Most 529 plans are limited to one fund family and restrict the number of investment strategy changes you can make each year.

Q *What if my child doesn't go to college or gets a free-ride scholarship?*

A If the beneficiary of the ESA or 529 doesn't use the money by age 30, you can change beneficiaries at any time and as often as you want. Siblings, parents, nieces, nephews—pretty much anyone in the family is eligible. However, if you decide to use the money for non-educational expenses, you'll pay a 10% penalty plus income taxes on the distribution. Some good news though: If your child's expenses are covered by scholarships and you withdraw money for non-qualified purchases, the 10% penalty does not apply.

hunting their new part-time job. Stay focused on saving, and don't panic. Remember, college is about education, not pedigree. And student loans are off-limits!

Start Saving Today!
Just like investing for retirement, the sooner you start saving for your kids' college, the more money you'll have when the time comes. If you're ready for Baby Step 5, don't wait any longer! An investing professional will help you make a college savings plan and help you choose mutual

> *"The sooner you start saving for your kids' college, the more money you'll have when the time comes."*

Q *What if my kid is already a teenager, and I'm just getting started?*

A If you have five years or less before your teen starts college, you need to take a savings, rather than investing, approach. That means piling up cash in a money market fund instead of using an ESA or 529. Your kid can also help make up the difference by making scholarship

funds for your ESA and/or 529. To help you sort through your options, you can work with a SmartVestor Pro in your area. This professional can answer your questions and help you understand what you're investing in.

Tell Your Story

Week 8

Does your current housing situation feel
more like a dream or a nightmare?

_____

_____

_____

_____

_____

_____

_____

_____

_____

_____

_____

_____

_____

DATE

REAL ESTATE AND MORTGAGES

KEEPING THE AMERICAN DREAM FROM BECOMING A NIGHTMARE

Homeownership is one of the biggest blessings we could ever experience. However, learning to navigate through the minefield of real estate and mortgages can be pretty daunting. With 40-year loans, interest-only options and reverse mortgages on the market, it's more important than ever to learn the ins and outs of personal real estate.

In *Real Estate and Mortgages*, Dave shares his most effective tips for buying and selling your home, and Chris breaks down the different mortgage options to reveal the best—and worst—ways to buy a house.

You don't pay off your house early by accident. This only happens if you've been diligently working that budget every month for several years.

BABY STEP 6

Pay off the house _____.

Renting

There is nothing wrong with _____ for a little while. This demonstrates _____ and wisdom.

However, renting should be a temporary situation, not your long-term plan!

And Jesus said to him, "Foxes have holes and birds of the air have nests, but the Son of Man has nowhere to lay His head."

—LUKE 9:58

When to Buy

Buying a house when you're not ready can be a disaster. You're only ready to buy if you are out of debt and have a fully funded emergency fund of 3–6 months of expenses. At that point, you can save for a big down payment. We call that Baby Step 3b.

Why to Buy

- It's a _____ savings plan.

- It's an _____ hedge.

- It grows virtually _____ _____.

What to Buy

Buy in the _____ price range of the neighborhood, and never overbuild your neighborhood through home additions and improvements.

Homes appreciate in good neighborhoods and are priced based on three things: _____, _____ and _____!

If possible, buy near _____ or with a _____.

Buy bargains by _____ bad landscaping, ugly carpet, outdated wallpaper and the Elvis print in the master bedroom.

Always buy a home that is (or can be) attractive from the _____ and has a good basic _____.

> *I had rather be on my farm than be emperor of the world.*
>
> – GEORGE WASHINGTON

How to Buy

Real estate _____ have full access to the Multiple Listing Service (MLS) and can make house hunting easier.

Search for a home using _____ listings.

Always get a land _____ if buying more than a standard subdivision lot.

Have the home inspected mechanically and structurally by a certified _____ _____.

Get an _____, but understand that it is just an opinion of value.

_____ insurance insures you against an unclean title, which is when your property ownership is called into question. It is a must-buy.

Mortgage Guidelines

First, remember to _____ debt.

The best plan is the _____%-down plan.

Get a monthly payment of no more than _____% of your take-home pay on a _____ fixed-rate loan, with at least _____% down.

According to the Census Bureau, 31% of homeowners have no mortgage debt of any type.

The best house payment is one really, really big one up front, and then no more after that! Pay cash! It is possible!

Why choose a **15-YEAR** mortgage?
(Figures based on 6% APR)

Let's say you buy a $225,000 house...
15-year mortgage = $1,899/month
30-year mortgage = $1,349/month

Fast-forward 10 years...
15-year mortgage has a balance of **$98,210**
30-year mortgage has a balance of **$188,292**

*During that 10 years, you would have paid almost $162,000 on the
30-year mortgage, but only paid down the loan by $36,708!*

> I knew a 15-year
> fixed-rate mortgage
> was the way to go, but
> now I really understand
> why it is so important on
> many levels.
>
> —Larry

Horrible Mortgage Options

- _____ – Adjustable-Rate Mortgages

    □ The concept of the ARM is to _____ the
    risk of higher interest rates to the
    _____, and, in return, the lender gives
    a lower rate now.

    □ If you have an ARM, refinance immediately!

- Of course, _____ - _____ loans are a
  bad idea because you are only paying the interest.

- _____ Mortgages

- _____, or Bi-Weekly Payoff
  Program

You should definitely pay off the mortgage as early as possible, but don't pay a fee for some special program that pays it off early! Just make extra principal payments on your own.

- _____ Advantages of a Mortgage

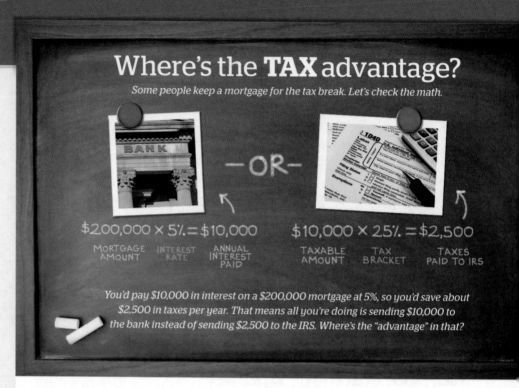

Where's the **TAX** advantage?

Some people keep a mortgage for the tax break. Let's check the math.

—OR—

$200,000 × 5% = $10,000
MORTGAGE · INTEREST · ANNUAL
AMOUNT · RATE · INTEREST PAID

$10,000 × 25% = $2,500
TAXABLE · TAX · TAXES
AMOUNT · BRACKET · PAID TO IRS

You'd pay $10,000 in interest on a $200,000 mortgage at 5%, so you'd save about $2,500 in taxes per year. That means all you're doing is sending $10,000 to the bank instead of sending $2,500 to the IRS. Where's the "advantage" in that?

Basic Ways to Finance a Home

_____ loans are usually through Fannie Mae and are privately insured against default.

PMI is _____ mortgage insurance.

_____ (Federal Housing Administration) loans are insured by HUD—the federal government.

- Down payments are as low as ____% and are used on lower-priced homes.

- These loans are currently _____ expensive than conventional financing and should be avoided.

PMI is there to protect the lender, not you. It costs about $70 a month per $100,000 borrowed. So if you have a $200,000 mortgage with PMI, you're paying about $140 extra every month.

However, if you put 20% down or pay your loan down to 80% loan-to-value, you can drop or remove PMI. Check with your mortgage company.

_____ loans are insured by the U.S. Department of Veterans Affairs.

- With a good down payment, the conventional loan is a _____ deal than the VA.

_____ financing is when you pay the owner over time, making him or her the mortgage holder.

- This is a _____ way to finance because you can be creative in the structure of the loan.

- Be extremely careful with owner financing—and make sure the whole deal is in writing!

Challenges and Opportunities

If you do what we teach, your credit score will eventually hit zero, which means you'll need to find a mortgage lender that does _____ underwriting.

> _Lenders still do manual underwriting, but they're getting fewer and farther between because it takes some extra effort on their part. If one bank tells you they can't do it, just keep looking._

When you owe more on your house than it is currently worth, you are _____ _____ on your home.

3 C's of Home Buying:

- Be cautious
- Be careful
- Be coherent

To qualify for manual underwriting, you'll need a solid, stable employment history as well as records showing at least two years of paying rent and utilities early or on time.

In a _____ sale, the home is sold for less than the amount owed, and the lienholder agrees to accept the proceeds from the home sale as payment in full without recourse.

This is a horrible and unethical way out of a bad mortgage situation. If you signed up for the loan, then you owe the money. It doesn't matter if the home has lost value or not.

Willfully walking away from a mortgage—even though you have the money to make the payments—is called _____ default.

Selling a Home

When selling a home, you should think like a _____.

The return on investment of fix-up dollars is _____.

The most important aspect of preparation is attention to _____ appeal.

When selling your home, make sure that it is listed on the _____.

When selling, statistical research has found that the best real estate agents are worth _____ than they cost, unless you are a seasoned pro.

90% of buyers use the internet to look at homes as part of their house hunting. That means 9 out of 10 buyers will know all about your house before they ever even make it to the curb.

—Better Homes and Gardens

The exposure through the _____ Listing Service is worth it.

When selecting an agent, do not rely on _____ or _____.

You should _____ at least three real estate agents.

Have your agent do a detailed Comparative _____ Analysis (CMA) to accurately price your home.

Offering a home warranty will typically not make a sale. If the buyer asks for a warranty, then consider it with the offer.

One-Minute Takeaway

What jumped out at you in this lesson? How can this affect your story?

_____

_____

_____

_____

_____

Small Group Discussion

True life-change happens when you open up and work through this material together. Break up into discussion groups of no more than 20 people to talk through the following questions. Be honest in your answers!

1 Many American families are currently living in a home that they cannot afford. What are some situations that might cause someone to become "house poor," and what are some solutions?

2 There are often two extremes when it comes to renting: Some people think it is always a waste of money, and others choose renting as a long-term way of life. When is it a good idea to rent instead of buy? Why are we sometimes in such a rush to buy, even when we can't afford it?

3 Look at the "Housing" category on your zero-based budget. Based on your overall financial condition, would you consider your housing situation to be a blessing or a curse? Are you living the American Dream or teetering on the edge of an American Nightmare?

Breakout Group Exercise

Break into smaller groups of 4–5 people to work through the following activity. Choose a leader to read through the exercise aloud and keep the group on task. Your facilitator will call the groups back together to report your findings.

Case Study 1

This is an especially exciting season in Mark and Julia's life together. They have been married for five years, have two kids, and have spent the last three years getting out of debt and building up their emergency fund. They are now financially ready to stop renting and purchase their first home. The average home price is $200,000 in their area, and they are committed to staying within the guidelines they learned during *Financial Peace Military*.

As a group, let's help them make a wise financial decision.
Here are some details about their finances:

$ Mark and Julia have a **monthly take-home pay of $4,000**.

   They have **$10,000 in their Baby Step 3 emergency fund**.

   They have **$15,000 set aside for a down payment** (not including their emergency fund).

DISCUSSION QUESTIONS

1. Using the simple calculation taught in FPM determine the maximum monthly payment that Mark and Julia can afford.

2. If Mark and Julia decide to purchase a $200,000 home, what is the minimum down payment they'll need according to the mortgage guidelines outlined in this lesson?

3. Julia has calculated that it will take six more months to save up a sufficient down payment. Mark believes they should pull money out of their emergency fund and pay it back to themselves later, but Julia disagrees. Explain to your group what you think they should do and why.

Case Study 2

Brandon and Erin are in their mid-twenties and have been married for two years. They are both working and enjoy their careers, and they have decided to wait a few more years before having children. At that point, however, Erin wants to leave the workplace and be a stay-at-home mom. With this in mind, the couple wants to make the most of their dual incomes while they can.

Let's take a look at some specific elements of their finances:

$ *Income 1*: Brandon is an audio engineer at a local nonprofit radio station, and, after tithing, **he brings home $2,600 per month**.

$ *Income 2*: Erin is an advertising manager, and, after tithing, **she brings home $4,000 per month**.

Savings: The couple is **completely debt-free** with a **full emergency fund**.

Rent: They currently **rent** a one-bedroom apartment for **$600 per month**.

DISCUSSION QUESTIONS

1. Brandon and Erin have committed to live solely off of his income and save all of her income to buy a home with FPM's "100%-Down Plan." Assuming their incomes stay the same, how long will it take for them to save up to pay cash for a $160,000 home?

2. When Erin told her father what she and Brandon planned to do, he got extremely frustrated with them. He doesn't understand why they don't upgrade their older cars and "live a little" while they're young and still have two incomes. If you were Erin, what would you tell him?

3. Brandon and Erin's friends often take expensive vacations and go out to eat several nights a week. Discuss some ways Brandon and Erin can defend themselves against the temptation to stray from their plan "just this one time" as different opportunities arise. How can they keep their dream in front of them and stay gazelle intense over the course of many years?

Case Study 3

The following questions come from actual radio calls that Dave has taken on his daily radio program, *The Dave Ramsey Show*. While they may not be specific to real estate, these calls cover several different topics that we have discussed over the past several weeks.

As a group, your objective is to answer the calls the way you think Dave would. Once all the breakout groups have finished, each group will share their answers.

QUESTIONS

1. "How much life insurance does my husband need to carry if he makes $60,000 a year?" *—Suzanne on Facebook*

2. "My husband and I have four small children, and we are paying $600 a month for our health insurance—which we barely use. We are seriously considering canceling the whole policy and just saving up some cash to pay for medical care. What do you think?"
—Audrey in San Francisco

3. "Dave, why are you so against people buying brand-new cars unless they have a $1 million net worth?" *—Todd on Facebook*

4. "Dave, my wife has house fever! She's shopping online and wants to finance it 100%. She's angry with me because I won't agree to do it. What are some ways I can get through to her about this?"
—Alan in Amarillo

5. "Every year I get a large tax refund, and I've heard you say that it's not a smart thing to do. Can you help me understand why?"
—Jen on Facebook

This Week's Homework

Personal finance is 20% head knowledge and 80% behavior. Take charge of your financial behaviors by completing the following tasks this week. Be sure to work with your spouse or accountability partner where noted!

☑ **Calculate your mortgage payoff.**
What would it take for you to payoff your home?

☑ **Celebrate your financial turnaround.**
Fill out the Financial Reality Check on the next page or use the online version in the Military Toolkit. Be sure to bring the results to class next week.

Financial Reality Check

It's time to take another look at your progress! Reference your debt snowball and answer the following questions about how your financial situation has changed since the class started.

 ## How much non-mortgage debt have you paid off?

This is the total amount you've knocked out during FPM. Be sure to include all of your non-mortgage debts and any progress you've made on your debt snowball.

TOTAL

 ## How much money have you saved?

If you're working on Baby Steps 1-3, this represents your emergency fund savings. If you're on Baby Steps 4-7, this includes both emergency funds and any investments you've made during the class.

TOTAL

 ## How many credit cards have you closed and cut up?

Remember, even if you pay off a card, the account is still open. To truly be rid of it forever, you must formally request that the credit company or bank officially close the account.

TOTAL

 ## How has your charitable giving changed?

This includes your tithe and any other charitable donation you've made during the class.

○ Little to no change   ○ Giving substantially more   ○ Giving for the first time

On a scale of 1-10, rate the following emotions in regard to your personal finances:

Fear	○	○	○	○	○	○	○	○	○	○
Anxiety	○	○	○	○	○	○	○	○	○	○
Confidence	○	○	○	○	○	○	○	○	○	○
Hope	○	○	○	○	○	○	○	○	○	○
Peace	○	○	○	○	○	○	○	○	○	○
	1	2	3	4	5	6	7	8	9	10
	Practically None									Extremely High

Is a Mortgage Refinance Right for You?

When the real estate market is down, you'll hear a lot of hype about refinancing mortgages. They say things like, "Rates have never been lower!" or "Lock in now to save!" It's easy to get sucked in and think refinancing is the way to go.

But that's not always the case. Refinancing is a great option when you have the opportunity to get a lower rate on a more appealing mortgage. There's a little more to it than just that, though. And if you do refinance, you need to know how to go about doing it the right way.

Like anything else, you need to determine if a refinance is right for you based on the specifics of your mortgage. Here are some guidelines to get you started:

The Break-Even Analysis
A refinance makes sense when you can lower your interest rate enough to pay for the closing costs before you plan to sell your home.

Here's a simple example. If you have a $100,000 mortgage and you can lower your interest rate by 1% in a refinance, you'll save $1,000 a year. If your closing costs are $3,000, it will take three years to break even on your refinance.

Be realistic when you estimate how much longer you plan on being in your current home. How many more kids do you plan on having, and do you have enough bedrooms for them? Do you want a guest room, or are you comfortable converting it into a room for one of the kids? Ask yourself these types of questions when making that decision.

Points, ARMs and Seconds
When you're gathering quotes for a refinance, ask for a par quote or zero quote. That means the closing cost estimates will not include points or origination fees. Don't pay these fees, which are

simply pre-paid interest. The savings, if any, don't justify the up-front expense.

If you have an Adjustable-Rate Mortgage (ARM), Dave will almost always recommend you refinance into a fixed-rate mortgage. Even if you have to write a check to pay for the closing costs, it's worth it to avoid the risk that your payments could go up when the rate adjusts.

A lot of homeowners with a second mortgage want to roll it into their first

> *"Refinancing can be a great idea. But everyone's situation is different. You just need to make sure it works for you."*

mortgage with a refinance. Not so fast! If the balance on your second mortgage is less than half of your annual income, pay it off in Baby Step 2. If not, go ahead and refinance it with the first mortgage and pay it off in Baby Step 6.

Going From 30 to 15
When you buy a home, if you're not paying cash, you should get no more than a 15-year mortgage. However, if you already have a 30-year mortgage and a good rate, you don't have to go  to the expense of refinancing just to get the shorter term. Just calculate what your monthly payment would be on a 15-year term and be disciplined about paying that amount.

That said, you'll get a better rate on a 15-year mortgage. So if you plan on being in your house for a while, it might make sense to look into a refinance. Just make sure you fully understand the terms of the new mortgage before you sign on the dotted line.

Refinancing can be a great idea. But everyone's situation is different. You just need to make sure it works for you. Don't make a "smart" decision now that will cost you down the road. Use some of these tips to make sure you understand the refinancing process and make the most out of your savings.

KEY TERMS

Adjustable-Rate Mortgage (ARM): Mortgage in which the interest rate changes periodically; a way for banks to transfer the risk of higher interest rates to the consumer

Curb Appeal: A home's degree of attractiveness from the perspective of a passerby

Comparative Market Analysis (CMA): A property's estimated value based on the actual sales price of similar properties

Equity: The value of a piece of property over and above any mortgage or liabilities related to it; basically, what you *own* minus what you *owe*

Fannie Mae (FNMA): The Federal National Mortgage Association, a privately owned corporation that trades in mortgages

Fixed Rate: An interest rate that does not change over time

Inflation Hedge: An asset that increases in value, which helps offset the rising inflation rate

Multiple Listing Service (MLS): Computer program used by real estate agents to search frequently updated listings of available properties

Mortgage: Loan secured by the collateral of real estate property

Private Mortgage Insurance (PMI): Insurance that protects the lender from default on a mortgage; usually required when the loan has less than 20% loan-to-value

Principal: Original amount of money invested, excluding any interest or dividends; also called the face value of a loan

Tell Your Story

Week 9

What story do you want your
money to tell about your life?

_____

_____

_____

_____

_____

_____

_____

_____

_____

_____

_____

DATE

THE **GREAT** MISUNDERSTANDING

UNLEASHING THE POWER OF GENEROUS GIVING

Why is it so important to take control over our money? Dave says there are only three things we can do with money: SPEND it (we've got that one down!), INVEST it (we're learning!), and GIVE it. What? How can we build wealth if we're constantly giving our money away? Dave calls that "The Great Misunderstanding," and it can change your life.

In *The Great Misunderstanding*, Dave discusses the commonly held misperceptions many people have about giving and reveals the true key to winning—with both your life and your money.

BABY STEP 7

Build wealth and

_____.

You can do everything we teach and you will prosper, but if you don't understand this lesson, you will never have _____ _____.

The Great Misunderstanding, the paradox, is the mistaken belief that the way to have _____ is to hold on _____.

You will never have financial peace until you learn to manage money with an open hand.

Owners and Managers

You and I are asset _____ for the
_____, so if we view it properly, we aren't giving
our own money away.

> *The earth is the Lord's, and the fulness thereof.*
>
> —PSALM 24:1 (KJV)

A _____ is a manager, not an _____.

God owns the
WHOLE THING—
not just a tithe.

*A good man leaves
an inheritance
to his children's
children.*

—PROVERBS 13:22

What Happens When We Give?

Why does the Bible tell us to _____ so often?

Giving makes us more Christ-like; a spiritually mature
Christian gives.

> *For God so loved the world that He gave His only
> begotten Son, that whoever believes in Him should not
> perish but have everlasting life.*
>
> —JOHN 3:16

The Bible talks about money more
often than it talks about love and
grace. Think our attitude about money
might be a big deal to God?

Giving moves you to become less _____,
and less-selfish people have more of a tendency to
_____ in relationships and wealth.

Because we are designed in God's image, we are
happiest and most fulfilled when _____
and _____.

66
*I don't know what your
destiny will be, but one
thing I know. The ones
among you who will be
really happy are those
who have sought and
found how to serve.*

—ALBERT SCHWEITZER

The offering shouldn't be a "halftime" break during the worship service. It's not intermission; it's part of worship.

Why Give?

Giving is a _____ of _____.

Giving is _____ and _____.

Giving is _____ _____.

> *"And I will rebuke the devourer for your sakes, so that he will not destroy the fruit of your ground, nor shall the vine fail to bear fruit for you in the field," says the LORD of hosts.*
>
> —MALACHI 3:11

Tithes and Offerings

The tithe is a tenth of your _____.

The Bible says to give your "firstfruits," meaning off the _____.

The tithe is to go to your _____ _____, which provides the same function as the Old Testament _____.

- Your pastor should be paid well!

- Your church should be taking care of widows, orphans and single parents. And in this day and age, that includes the families of deployed military personnel!

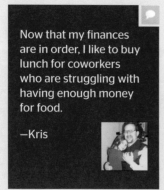

Now that my finances are in order, I like to buy lunch for coworkers who are struggling with having enough money for food.

—Kris

_____ are different than the tithe. They are above the tithe and are freely given from _____.

Never give with the _____ of having your giving _____.

Financial Peace is more than just God's system for understanding money, becoming debt-free, and building wealth.

Financial Peace is when The Great Misunderstanding is _____.

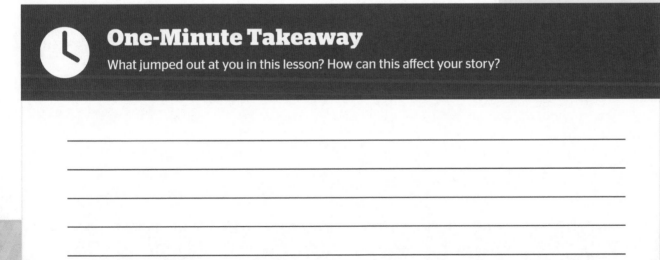

One-Minute Takeaway

What jumped out at you in this lesson? How can this affect your story?

_____

_____

_____

_____

_____

Small Group Discussion

True life-change happens when you open up and work through this material together. Break up into discussion groups of no more than 20 people to talk through the following questions. Be honest in your answers!

1 Dave stresses the importance of giving no matter what Baby Step you're on. Why does Dave encourage someone to give off the top of their budget, even if they have debt?

2 Psalm 24:1 (KJV) says, "The earth is the Lord's, and the fulness thereof." What would happen in the world if everyone started looking at their money and possessions as belonging to God, not themselves? How could that impact the church?

3 Dave says that giving is some of the most fun you can ever have with money. Has anyone ever surprised you with a meaningful act of giving? Have you ever experienced the joy of giving in a big way?

4 Look back over the past nine weeks and think about what you've learned and how your life has changed as a result of participating in FPM. Tell the group how your life is different now compared to where you started. What are some ways you could "pay it forward" to someone else?

This Week's Homework

Personal finance is 20% head knowledge and 80% behavior. Take charge of your financial behaviors by completing the following tasks this week. Be sure to work with your spouse or accountability partner where noted!

☑ **Pray about giving.**
Prayerfully consider what the Bible teaches about giving as presented in this lesson. Using your budget, determine how giving biblically would impact your financial life. Adjust your budget to accommodate any changes you need to make.

☑ **Discuss the word "blessing."**
Singles: Read Malachi 3:10–12 and talk with your accountability partner about what the word "blessing" might mean in light of this lesson. Discuss any budget changes you are considering as a result.

Married Couples: Read Malachi 3:10–12 together and discuss what the word "blessing" might mean in light of this lesson. Review your budget to determine what changes you could or should make as a result.

☑ **Keep going!**
Do a zero-based budget every month for the rest of your life! You can also stay current by checking out new information and updates online, and you can take this class again as many times as you want at no extra cost!

6 Questions About Giving

Dave's three big principles are save, spend and give. We want you to enjoy your saving and spending, but giving is really some of the most fun you can have with money. We get a lot of questions on the topic though, so let's take a look at the most common ones.

1 What's the point of tithing?
God doesn't need our money. He owns the cattle on a thousand hills. That's not why He repeatedly tells us to give and have an eternal view of everything He's given us. His desire is that we'd experience the kind of peace that comes from a content heart.

Having a content heart, managing money God's way, and avoiding the temptation of materialism frees us to focus on the things that really matter—like family, friends and, ultimately, changing our family tree.

2 Should you stop tithing when money's tight?
The Bible does not mention anything about putting a hold on your tithing. And it never implies that tithing is a salvation issue.

The tithe, which is a scriptural mandate, was not instituted for God's benefit, because He already has all the money He needs. He does not need our money.

So why does He ask us to give 10% to Him? Tithing was created for our benefit. It is to teach us how to keep God first in our lives and how to be unselfish people. Unselfish people make better husbands, wives, friends, relatives, employees and employers. God is trying to teach us how to prosper over time.

If you cannot live off 90% of your income, then you probably cannot live off 100%. Something is already off in your plan. And if you do tithe, do it out of love for God, not guilt.

3 Is it right to count my church tithes on my tax returns?
You gave the money to the church. You were biblically obedient in that. The Bible also tells us to be good managers of our money. It does not diminish the sanctity of your gift to take the tax deduction. It is a way to manage the rest of the money. Take the deduction.

Later, if you get an income tax refund, remember that this is money that you've already tithed. But you can always choose to give some or all of it back to the Lord as additional thanks for His blessings.

4 I'm making more money now. How should I increase my giving above the tithe?

When things are going well, it's easy to accidentally spend all the extra income. That's why Dave recommends that you name each of those new dollars in your budget every month.

Set up your budget based on your new salary, including your giving, spending and saving. Then, any additional income is divided among extra giving, extra investing and some blow money.

5 Can't I also volunteer my time and services as a form of giving?

Absolutely! You can serve food at a homeless shelter, read stories to the elderly at a nursing home, help with parking or child care at your church—the list could go on and on. You can also look for special opportunities to help people in need, like a lady who has a flat tire on the side of the road or a young married couple who just had their first baby.

This doesn't have to be a formula or a checklist of ways to give. All you need to do is start with an attitude of thankfulness, generosity and giving, and that attitude will reflect how you respond in everyday life.

6 Can you give too much?

Sure. The Bible says to give a tenth of your income to your local church. Your first goal after the tithe is to take care of your household. Then, above that, to support other ministries with your giving. But you definitely shouldn't be giving yourself into the poorhouse. When you have a better financial foundation in a few years, you are more free to give above the tithe.

"Bottom line: Giving liberates the soul of the giver. A giver never walks away feeling badly."

Bottom line: Giving liberates the soul of the giver. A giver never walks away feeling badly. Whether through a tithe, charitable contribution or gift  to a friend in need, giving not only generates good—it brings contentment.

As we've seen throughout FPM, money is never *just* about money. It is about so much more. When giving becomes part of our natural way of life, incredible blessings are unlocked in our spirit that we've never even imagined! It's a great way to live!

You
DID IT!

So this is the end of your FPM class—but it's only the beginning of your story. In fact, this is where your story *really* takes off!

You're now part of a family of millions who have learned how to handle money God's ways. You've taken responsibility for yourself and your family. You've committed to becoming the godly steward God designed you to be. Wherever you are in the Baby Steps today, you can be sure of one thing: From this point forward, you are now winning with money. And we applaud you.

We've covered a lot of ground together over the past nine weeks, and we know it can all be a little overwhelming. That's okay. Just take one step at a time, stay motivated, and *keep going*. And always remember, "If you will live like no one else, later you can live—and give—*like no one else*."

Now go do it!

MONTHLY BUDGETING FORMS

Welcome to the wonderful world of cash flow management! By filling out just a few forms, your new financial plan will start to unfold right in front of you. You'll immediately identify problem areas and learn how to close the valve of wasteful spending, because you'll know exactly where all of your dollars are going!

It will take a little while to fill these forms for the first time. That's because you'll be doing something you've probably never done, and you'll be facing behaviors you may have never faced. That's okay! After that initial start-up, however, you'll get better and better at this until budgeting feels like second nature.

For monthly budgeting, you'll just need to use two forms: the Monthly Cash Flow Plan along with the Allocated Spending Plan or Irregular Income Plan, depending on how you get paid. This should just take about 30 minutes a month once you get in the habit.

Dave covers these three forms in detail in the Cash Flow Planning lesson, and we also have tutorials online for each budget form. If you need a little help as you fill out the forms, just take a breath and check out one of those helpful resources.

Are you ready? It's time to make those dollars dance! Go for it!

Monthly Cash Flow Plan

Cash flows in and out each month. Make sure you tell it where to go!

Yes, this budget form has a lot of lines and blanks.

But that's okay. We do that so we can list practically every expense imaginable on this form to prevent you from forgetting something. Don't expect to put something on every line. Just use the ones that are relevant to your specific situation.

Step 1

Enter your monthly take-home pay in the box at the top right (**A**). This is the amount you have for the month to budget. So far so good, huh?

Step 2

Within each main category, such as Food, there are subcategories, like Groceries. Start at the top and work your way down, filling out the Budgeted column (**B**) first. Add up each subcategory and put that number in the Total box (**C**).

Also, pay attention to Dave's recommended percentages (**D**). This will help you keep from budgeting too much for a category.

Step 3

Finally, enter your take-home pay in the top box at the end of the page (**E**), then add up all categories and place that total in the Category Totals box (**F**). Then subtract your Category Totals amount from your Take-Home Pay. You should have a zero balance (**G**). Doesn't that feel great?

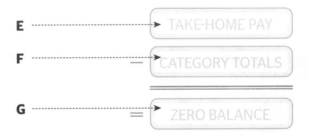

Step 4

When the month ends, put what you actually spent in the Spent column (**H**). That will help you make any necessary adjustments to the next month's budget.

Monthly Cash Flow Plan

Cash flows in and out each month. Make sure you tell it where to go!

Monthly Take-Home Pay [   ]

Add up budgeted column & enter here

These icons represent good options for cash envelopes

♥ CHARITY

	Spent	Budgeted
Tithes		
Charity & Offerings		
10-15%	TOTAL	

🐖 SAVING

	Spent	Budgeted
Emergency Fund		
Retirement Fund		
College Fund		
10-15%	TOTAL	

🏠 HOUSING

	Spent	Budgeted
First Mortgage/Rent		
Second Mortgage		
Real Estate Taxes		
Repairs/Maint.		
Association Dues		
25-35%	TOTAL	

⚙ UTILITIES

	Spent	Budgeted
Electricity		
Gas		
Water		
Trash		
Phone/Mobile		
Internet		
Cable		
5-10%	TOTAL	

🍎 FOOD

	Spent	Budgeted
✉ Groceries		
✉ Restaurants		
5-15%	TOTAL	

👕 CLOTHING

	Spent	Budgeted
✉ Adults		
✉ Children		
✉ Cleaning/Laundry		
2-7%	TOTAL	

🚗 TRANSPORTATION

	Spent	Budgeted
Gas & Oil		
✉ Repairs & Tires		
License & Taxes		
Car Replacement		
Other _____		
10-15%	TOTAL	

⚕ MEDICAL/HEALTH

	Spent	Budgeted
Medications		
Doctor Bills		
Dentist		
Optometrist		
Vitamins		
Other _____		
Other _____		
5-10%	TOTAL	

*Dave's Recommended Percentages

🛡 INSURANCE

	Spent	Budgeted
Life Insurance		
Health Insurance		
Homeowner/Renter		
Auto Insurance		
Disability Insurance		
Identity Theft		
Long-Term Care		
*10-25% TOTAL		

👤 PERSONAL

	Spent	Budgeted
✉ Child Care/Sitter		
✉ Toiletries		
✉ Cosmetics/Hair Care		
Education/Tuition		
Books/Supplies		
Child Support		
Alimony		
Subscriptions		
Organization Dues		
Gifts (inc. Christmas)		
✉ Replace Furniture		
✉ Pocket Money (His)		
✉ Pocket Money (Hers)		
Baby Supplies		
Pet Supplies		
Music/Technology		
Miscellaneous		
Other _____		
Other _____		
*5-10% TOTAL		

🏃 RECREATION

	Spent	Budgeted
✉ Entertainment		
Vacation		
*5-10% TOTAL		

🔗 DEBTS

	Spent	Budgeted
Car Payment 1		
Car Payment 2		
Credit Card 1 _____		
Credit Card 2 _____		
Credit Card 3 _____		
Credit Card 4 _____		
Credit Card 5 _____		
Student Loan 1		
Student Loan 2		
Student Loan 3		
Student Loan 4		
Other _____		
Other _____		
Other _____		
Other _____		
Other _____		

Your goal is 0% → ***5-10%** TOTAL

Once you have completed filling out each category, subtract all category totals from your take-home pay.

Use the "income sources" form if necessary → TAKE-HOME PAY

Add up totals from each category − CATEGORY TOTALS

Remember— The goal of a zero-based budget is to get this number to zero = ZERO BALANCE

Allocated Spending Plan

Don't let this one scare you. Managing your money week to week happens here!

Life pulls your money in all directions. Spend time here before spending your cash.

Allocation is a fancy word for "when you spend your money." We're going to build on your Monthly Cash Flow Plan here and get a little more in depth by breaking your income down by pay period. The four columns on this form represent the four weeks in a given month. If you're married, combine your spouse's income with yours.

Step 1a

Fill out the pay period in box **A**. This is simply how long you'll go between paychecks. If you get paid on the 1st and 15th, then your pay period for July, for example, would be 7/1 to 7/14.

Step 1b

Write how much you will be paid in that pay period (**B**).

A ....

Pay Period Dates	TO
Pay Period Income	

B ....

Step 2

Write down how much money you're budgeting in the Budgeted column (**C**). In the Remaining column (**D**), keep a running total of how much of your starting income you have left for that pay period.

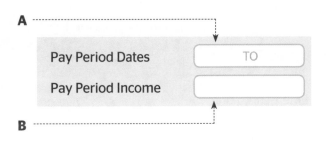

🏠 HOUSING	Budgeted	Remaining
First Mortgage/Rent	945	285
Second Mortgage		
Real Estate Taxes	150	135

Step 3

Keep going down the list until the "Remaining" column (**E**) hits zero. When "Remaining" equals zero, you're done budgeting for that pay period.

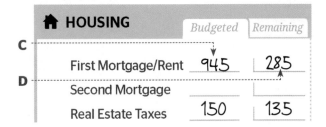

	Budgeted	Remaining
Optometrist	40	95
Vitamins	20	75
Other _____		
Other _____		

Step 4

If you have money left over at the end of the column (**F**), go back and adjust an area, such as savings or giving, so that you spend every single dollar. Every dollar needs a home.

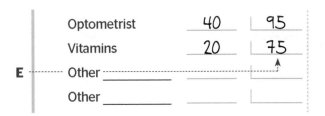

	Budgeted	Remaining
Other Final cable bill	40	35
Other Florist bill	35	0
Other _____		

Allocated Spending Plan

Don't let this one scare you. Managing your money week to week happens here!

	TO	TO	TO	TO
Pay Period Dates				
Pay Period Income				

↑ Income
— Tithes
= Remaining to budget this pay period

♥ CHARITY

	Budgeted	Remaining	Budgeted	Remaining	Budgeted	Remaining	Budgeted	Remaining
Tithes								
Charity & Offerings								

"Remaining" minus "Budgeted." Back & forth.

🐷 SAVING

	Budgeted	Remaining	Budgeted	Remaining	Budgeted	Remaining	Budgeted	Remaining
Emergency Fund								
Retirement Fund								
College Fund								

🏠 HOUSING

	Budgeted	Remaining	Budgeted	Remaining	Budgeted	Remaining	Budgeted	Remaining
First Mortgage/Rent								
Second Mortgage								
Real Estate Taxes								
Repairs/Maint.								
Association Dues								
Other _____								

⚙ UTILITIES

	Budgeted	Remaining	Budgeted	Remaining	Budgeted	Remaining	Budgeted	Remaining
Electricity								
Gas								
Water								
Trash								
Phone/Mobile								
Internet								
Cable								
Other _____								

Pay Period Dates	TO	TO	TO	TO

When "Remaining" equals zero, you're done budgeting for this pay period.

🍎 FOOD

	Budgeted	Remaining	Budgeted	Remaining	Budgeted	Remaining	Budgeted	Remaining
✉ Groceries								
✉ Restaurants								

👕 CLOTHING

	Budgeted	Remaining	Budgeted	Remaining	Budgeted	Remaining	Budgeted	Remaining
✉ Adults								
✉ Children								
✉ Cleaning/Laundry								

🚗 TRANSPORTATION

	Budgeted	Remaining	Budgeted	Remaining	Budgeted	Remaining	Budgeted	Remaining
Gas and Oil								
✉ Repairs and Tires								
License and Taxes								
Car Replacement								
Other _____								
Other _____								

🩺 MEDICAL/HEALTH

	Budgeted	Remaining	Budgeted	Remaining	Budgeted	Remaining	Budgeted	Remaining
Medications								
Doctor Bills								
Dentist								
Optometrist								
Vitamins								
Other _____								
Other _____								
Other _____								
Other _____								

Allocated Spending Plan

Don't let this one scare you. Managing your money week to week happens here!

Pay Period Dates	TO	TO	TO	TO

🛡 INSURANCE

	Budgeted	Remaining	Budgeted	Remaining	Budgeted	Remaining	Budgeted	Remaining
Life Insurance								
Health Insurance								
Homeowner/Renter								
Auto Insurance								
Disability Insurance								
Identity Theft								
Long-Term Care								

👤 PERSONAL

	Budgeted	Remaining	Budgeted	Remaining	Budgeted	Remaining	Budgeted	Remaining
✉ Child Care/Sitter								
✉ Toiletries								
✉ Cosmetics								
Education/Tuition								
Books/Supplies								
Child Support								
Alimony								
Subscriptions								
Org. Dues								
Gifts (inc. Christmas)								
✉ Replace Furniture								
✉ Pocket Money (His)								
✉ Pocket Money (Hers)								
Baby Supplies								
Pet Supplies								
Music/Technology								
Miscellaneous								
Other _____								
Other _____								

Pay Period Dates	TO	TO	TO	TO

⚘ RECREATION

	Budgeted	Remaining	Budgeted	Remaining	Budgeted	Remaining	Budgeted	Remaining
✉ Entertainment								
Vacation								

⚒ DEBTS

	Budgeted	Remaining	Budgeted	Remaining	Budgeted	Remaining	Budgeted	Remaining
Car Payment 1								
Car Payment 2								
Credit Card 1 _____								
Credit Card 2 _____								
Credit Card 3 _____								
Credit Card 4 _____								
Credit Card 5 _____								
Student Loan 1								
Student Loan 2								
Student Loan 3								
Student Loan 4								
Other _____								
Other _____								
Other _____								
Other _____								
Other _____								
Other _____								
Other _____								
Other _____								
Other _____								
Other _____								
Other _____								
Other _____								
Other _____								

Irregular Income Planning

If you have an irregular income, this form just became your best friend!

Some people's paychecks all look the same, and some people's don't.
If you're self-employed or in sales, you really understand this! But you're not free from filling out budgets. As a matter of fact, this form is vital for just that reason! It can be easy for debts and expenses to overtake what you're bringing in. Stay on top of your money here.

Step 1

Fill in the Monthly Cash Flow Plan form based on what you reasonably expect to bring home for the month. If you aren't sure, use last year's lowest income month as your starting point.

Step 2

List anything that didn't make it in your Monthly Cash Flow Plan in the Items column (**A**). These are the things that you couldn't budget for but need to be funded.

ITEMS
A ----> Hospital Bill – Snowball
Home Depot – Snowball
Extra Entertainment

Step 3

Rewrite your expenses in priority order and keep a running total. Setting good priorities is crucial here. For instance, a beach trip is not more important than putting food on the table!

BUDGETED	RUNNING TOTAL
460	+ 460
1,000	= 1,460
50	1,510

Step 4

When you get paid, write any additional income in the box (**B**). "Additional" means anything above and beyond what you budgeted on the Monthly Cash Flow Plan form.

Additional Irregular Income	1,500

B

Step 5

Spend your money right down the list until it's all gone. You most likely won't make it all the way down the list. That's okay! That's why it's important to prioritize.

BUDGETED	RUNNING TOTAL
460	+ 460
1,000	= 1,460
~~50~~ 40	~~1,540~~ 1,500

Irregular Income Planning

If you have an irregular income, this form just became your best friend!

Any additional irregular income goes here

Additional Irregular Income

List, in priority order, anything that didn't make it in your monthly cash flow plan

Work back & forth, adding each budgeted item to the running total

ITEMS	BUDGETED	RUNNING TOTAL
		+
		=

ADDITIONAL FORMS

TAKE TOTAL CONTROL OF YOUR MONEY WITH THE COMPLETE SET OF BUDGET FORMS!

Once you get the hang of monthly budgeting with the basic forms, there are a few more steps to take to get the full picture of your financial situation.

To get a full, complete view of your finances, we recommend completing the entire set of forms up front, and then updating the set once a year. You'll also want to update the entire set any time you experience a dramatic positive or negative financial event, such as receiving a large inheritance or paying for an expensive home repair.

Each form has an explanation for what it is for, along with instructions for how to quickly and easily record the information. If you have any questions or need any help, just check out our tutorials online. We have detailed tutorials for every budget form.

Have fun!

Quick-Start Budget

Your first budget! It's also the simplest, so you can relax now.

It's time to get your feet wet with budgeting.

This form is only one page, but it will show you how much money you need every month to cover necessities. While your mortgage or rent is listed here, we won't get into the details of your credit card bills, student loans, car payments and any other debt yet. The Quick-Start Budget is just your starting point.

Step 1

Write down what you're spending for the month in each of the categories listed (**A**). If you don't know exactly, just make your best guess. We're keeping it simple for now.

A ---------

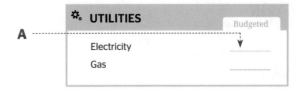

Step 2

Write the total for each category in the Total box (**B**) and move on to the next category. See? Easy!

B ---------

Step 3

Add up all eight of your total boxes and enter that number at the bottom in the Category Totals box (**C**). This shows you how much you're spending in a month for your basic necessities, not including any kind of debt. We'll get to all that later.

C ---------

Quick-Start Budget

Taking control of your money starts here!

Add up budgeted column & enter here

These icons represent good options for cash envelopes

♥ CHARITY

Budgeted

Tithes _____

TOTAL _____

🐷 SAVING

Budgeted

Emergency Fund _____

Other _____ _____

TOTAL _____

🏠 HOUSING

Budgeted

First Mortgage/Rent _____

Second Mortgage _____

Real Estate Taxes _____

Repairs/Maint. _____

Homeowner/Renter Ins. _____

TOTAL _____

⚙ UTILITIES

Budgeted

Electricity _____

Gas _____

Water _____

Trash _____

Phone/Mobile _____

Internet _____

Cable _____

TOTAL _____

🍎 FOOD

Budgeted

✉ Groceries _____

TOTAL _____

👕 CLOTHING

Budgeted

✉ Adults _____

✉ Children _____

TOTAL _____

🚗 TRANSPORTATION

Budgeted

Car Payment _____

Car Payment _____

Gas & Oil _____

✉ Repairs & Tires _____

Auto Insurance _____

TOTAL _____

🧍 PERSONAL

Budgeted

Life Insurance _____

Health Insurance _____

Disability Insurance _____

✉ Child Care/Sitter _____

✉ Entertainment _____

Other _____ _____

Other _____ _____

TOTAL _____

Add up totals from all categories CATEGORY TOTALS

Debt Snowball

Get the ball rolling and start attacking your debt!

You've got your emergency fund taken care of. Now it's time to dump the debt!

The Debt Snowball form will help you get some quick wins and develop some serious momentum! You'll make minimum payments on all of your debts except for the smallest one. Then, attack that one with gazelle intensity! Throw every dollar at it that you can!

Step 1

List your debts in order from the smallest Total Payoff" balance to the largest. Don't be concerned with interest rates, unless two debts have a similar payoff balance. In that case, list the one with the higher interest rate first.

DEBTS	TOTAL PAYOFF
Diagnostic	50
Hospital Bill	460
Home Depot	770

Step 2

Attack that smallest debt by paying as much on it as you possibly can. Once you pay one debt off, take what you *were* paying on that one and add it to the minimum payment of the *next* debt. As the snowball rolls over, it picks up more snow. Get it?

MIN. PAYMENT	NEW PAYMENT
~~10~~	~~10~~
~~38~~	+ ~~48~~
45	= 93

Step 3

Every time you pay off a debt, cross the debt off. This will show you how close you're getting to becoming debt-free!

~~Hospital Bill~~
~~Home Depot~~
~~Chase VISA~~ I'M DEBT-
~~Car Loan~~ FREE!!!!!

Debt Snowball

Get the ball rolling and start attacking your debt!

List your debts smallest to largest by balance

Once a debt is paid off, add the next minimum payment to your current amount. This becomes the new payment.

DEBTS	TOTAL PAYOFF	MIN. PAYMENT	NEW PAYMENT
			+
			=

Breakdown of Savings

This form will save you some headaches down the road. Plan ahead here.

These items are also called sinking funds. These are the safety nets in your plan.
After fully funding your emergency fund, start saving for other items, like furniture, cars, home maintenance or a vacation. This sheet will remind you that every dollar in your savings account is already committed to something.

Amount you have in each sinking fund

Your target balance for each sinking fund

ITEMS	BALANCE	TARGET
Emergency Fund (1) $1,000		
Emergency Fund (2) 3–6 Months		
Retirement Fund		
College Fund		
Real Estate Taxes		
Homeowner's Insurance		
Repairs/Maintenance Fee		
Replace Furniture		
Car Insurance		
Car Replacement		
Disability Insurance		
Health Insurance		
Doctor		
Dentist		
Optometrist		
Life Insurance		
School Tuition/Supplies		
Gifts (Including Christmas)		
Vacation		
Computer Replacement		
Tires		
Baby		
Other_____		

TOTAL

Consumer Equity Sheet

Here's where you can own up to what you have, and even what has you!

Your net worth: what you own minus what you owe.

Use this form to list all of your assets and their value. Then subtract what, if anything, you owe on each one. When you total the columns, the "Total Equity" box at the bottom shows your net worth.

How much each item is worth

How much you owe on each item

subtract debt from value to get equity

ITEMS	VALUE	—	DEBT	=	EQUITY
Real Estate _____					
Real Estate _____					
Car _____					
Car _____					
Cash On Hand					
Checking Account					
Savings Account					
Money Market Account					
Mutual Funds					
Retirement Plan					
Cash Value (Insurance)					
Household Items					
Jewelry					
Antiques					
Boat					
Unsecured Debt (Negative)					
Credit Card Debt (Negative)					
Other _____					
Other _____					

This is your net worth

TOTAL VALUE	—	TOTAL DEBT	=	TOTAL EQUITY

Lump Sum Payment Form

Hey, let's face it. We all take our lumps sometimes. It's life! But we can still be ready!

Plan for the big once- or twice-a-year payments.

This is the form for the payments you make on a non-monthly basis, like insurance premiums and taxes. They can be budget busters if you don't plan for them every month.

When this item comes due, how much will you need to cover it?

Use the formula below to find how much to budget

This amount goes into your monthly budget form

ITEM NEEDED	AMOUNT NEEDED	÷	MONTHS	=	BUDGETED
Real Estate Taxes					
Homeowner's Insurance					
Home Repairs					
Replace Furniture					
Medical Bills					
Health Insurance					
Life Insurance					
Disability Insurance					
Car Insurance					
Car Repair/Tags					
Replace Car					
Clothing					
Tuition					
Bank Note					
IRS (Self-Employed)					
Vacation					
Gifts (Including Christmas)					
Other					
Other					
Other					

Major Components
of a Healthy Financial Plan

Your financial plan has a lot of moving parts.

So you have to know what you need to do and when you need to do it. This form shows you the essential things that absolutely must be part of any successful plan. Go line by line and note what action you need to take for each item, then put a deadline on it.

ITEM	ACTION NEEDED	ACTION DATE
Written Cash Flow Plan		
Will or Estate Plan		
Debt Reduction Plan		
Tax Reduction Plan		
Emergency Funding		
Retirement Funding		
College Funding		
Charitable Giving		
Teach My Children		
Life Insurance		
Health Insurance		
Disability Insurance		
Auto Insurance		
Homeowner's Insurance		
Renter's Insurance		
Long-Term Care Insurance		
Identity Theft Insurance		

Recommended Percentages

You nerds will love this one! Calculate how you compare to these suggestions.

How much of your money should go where?

We've got some recommendations based on experience and research. If you find that you spend much more in one category than we recommend, consider adjusting your lifestyle in that area in order to enjoy more freedom and flexibility across the board. These are only suggestions though. For example, if you have a higher income, your percentage for things like food will be lower.

Use this formula to get your target percentages

Total monthly Income **X** Recommended Percentage

Use this formula to get your actual percentages

Budgeted Amount **÷** Total monthly Income **X** 100

ITEM	RECOMMENDED %	TARGET	ACTUAL
Charitable Gifts	10–15%		
Saving	10–15%		
Housing	25–35%		
Utilities	5–10%		
Food	5–15%		
Transportation	10–15%		
Clothing	2–7%		
Medical/Health	5–10%		
Insurance	10–25%		
Personal	5–10%		
Recreation	5–10%		
Debts	5–10%		

Income Sources Recap

Jot down your streams of income, even if it's just a trickle right now.

Money's fun. If you've got some.

You've got money coming in from somewhere, right? Then write it down. This form documents every single income source you've got. There's no such thing as "found money." It all counts, and it all goes on the budget!

Enter the amount of each income item here

Enter the date or pay period it will arrive

EMPLOYMENT	AMOUNT	ARRIVAL DATE
Paycheck 1		
Paycheck 2		
Commissions		
Bonus		
Self-Employment		
Tax Refund		
Other _____		

INVESTMENTS/RETIREMENT		
Interest Income		
Dividend Income		
Rental Income		
Trust Fund		
Social Security		
Pension		
Annuity		
Other _____		

OTHER		
Disability Income		
Alimony		
Child Support		
TANF		
Cash Gifts		
Unemployment		
Other _____		

Add up & enter total Income

TOTAL

Pro Rata Debt List

The best way to beat debt is with a calculated formula! Go!

"But I can't pay the minimum payments!" It's okay. We have a plan for that.

"Pro rata" means "fair share." Use this form to figure out what percentage of your income each creditor represents, and then send their payment along with a copy of this form and your budget every month—even if they say they won't accept it.

Step 1

Subtract Necessity Expense (**B**) from Household Income (**A**). That gives you your Disposable Income (**C**). That's how much money you have to pay toward debt after you've covered all your necessities.

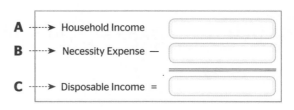

Step 2

Write in your Total Debt (**D**). Then collect all your bills and add up the grand total of all your monthly minimum payments. Write that in Total Min. Payments (**E**). If your Total Min. Payments figure is higher than your Disposable Income (**C**) figure, you need to use the Pro Rata Debt List.

ITEM	PAYOFF	÷	TOTAL DEBT	=	PERCENT	X	DISP. INC.	=	NEW PMT.
F	G		H		I		J		K

Step 3

List each debt in the Item (**F**) column and write the total debt payoff amount in the Payoff (**G**) column. Go ahead and write in the Total Debt (**H**) and Disposable Income—or Disp. Inc. (**J**)—amounts from the top of the form too.

Step 4

On each line, divide the Payoff (**G**) by the Total Debt (**H**) to get the Percent (**I**). That figure shows you each creditor's fair share of your available income.

Step 5

Multiply the Percent (**I**) by your total disposable income in the Disp. Inc. (**J**) column. Write that in the New Pmt. (**K**) column. That's what you should send to that specific creditor. Repeat that math for every item on the list to calculate your pro rata payments for each one.

Pro Rata Debt List

The best way to beat debt is with a calculated formula! Go!

Household Income   [_____]

Necessity Expense — [_____]

Disposable Income = [_____]

Don't include consumer debt payments

Add up the total debt column & enter total here

Total Debt   [_____]

Total Min. Payments [_____]

Add up all your minimum payments & enter here

Use the formula below to find your new payment

ITEM	PAYOFF	÷ TOTAL DEBT	= PERCENT	x DISP. INC.	= NEW PMT.

Credit Card History

We all have our histories. It's okay! List yours here.

Every lineup has the usual suspects.

And these usual suspects are thieves. Use this form to list every single credit card you have, including store cards. If you have no outstanding balance, close the account completely. If you still owe a balance, cut up the cards and pay them off using the Debt Snowball form!

Creditor's mailing address and phone number

Date you called to close the account

Confirmation number showing the account was closed

CARD TYPE	NUMBER	ADDRESS	PHONE	CLOSED	CONF.

Insurance Coverage

We all need the right insurance! Get it and record it.

Let's hear it for the unsung heroes of your financial plan.

Without proper insurance, certain losses will bankrupt you. Use this form to list all of your coverages, your plan numbers, and the contact information for your agents. Make sure your spouse or accountability partner knows where to find this form in case of emergency!

This form will help you keep track of all your insurance policies. Be sure to update any changes!

TYPE	COMPANY	PLAN ID #	COVERAGE	AGENT/PHONE	PREMIUM